PREFACE

This book is based on a series of client information handouts produced by Dr. Shawn Messonnier for North America. Lifelearn Limited and I have developed and expanded them specifically for the UK.

We have used Exotic Pets as a collective title but the book includes many pets which are very familiar such as hamsters, guinea pigs, rabbits and tortoises. The popularity of exotic pets has increased dramatically over the last few years and information on their welfare, husbandry and veterinary care is available but usually . in a variety of breed society pamphlets and individual breed books. This book is aimed predominantly at veterinary nurses, who are required to have a knowledge of exotic pets for their veterinary nursing qualifications, by the Royal College of Veterinary Surgeons. The topics covered are pet selection, anatomy, feeding, housing, common diseases and special problems. The veterinary nurse has a key role in informing clients of good husbandry for their pet and of problems to anticipate. Owners and veterinary students as well as veterinary nurses will also find much useful information. The majority of problems encountered by a veterinary practice dealing with exotic pets are caused by poor husbandry. I hope this book will encourage a greater understanding by veterinary nurses, veterinary students and owners.

Veterinary checks for new pets and yearly examinations for some species have been suggested in this book. We hope that this will encourage owners of exotic pets and their veterinary surgeons to give them the same level of attention that is afforded dogs and cats.

Further reading and useful addresses are provided for those requiring more information.

David L Williams MA VetMB PhD CertVOphthal MRCVS

Copyright © 1998 Lifelearn Limited

P.O. Box 16
Newmarket
Suffolk CB8 7TH

© Illustrations: Stephen M. Ricketts (1998)
Sub-editing: Susan M. Wreford

ISBN: 0 9532889 0 0

Acknowledgement

Lifelearn Limited would like to thank Susan Wreford for converting information from the client handouts into book form and Stephen Ricketts for illustrating.

The project was co-ordinated by Jenny Ricketts.

Cover: The publishers would like to thank Tiana Parry and her rabbit Benjamin for allowing their picture to be used and Geoff Evans, Sarah Hardcastle, Gill Povey and David Williams for providing the photographs.

The tables of normal biological information have been reproduced from The Manual of Exotic Pets (1991) P. H. Beynon & J. E. Cooper with permission of the B.S.A.V.A.

Published by   **Lifelearn Limited**
P.O. Box 16
Newmarket
Suffolk CB8 7TH

To purchase additional copies of this book tel: 01638 577822; fax: 01638 577975

Typeset and Printed by Premier Printers Bury St Edmunds.

TABLE OF CONTENTS

Page No.

TABLES

LINE DRAWINGS

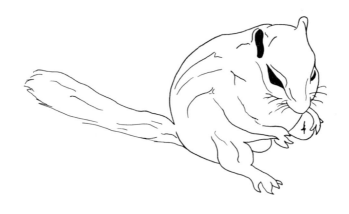

RODENTS

AND OTHER

MAMMALS

CHINCHILLAS

Chinchillas can make fun, enjoyable pets. They are rodents related to guinea pigs and originate from South America where they live in the Andes mountains. In addition to being popular as pets, they are raised commercially for their soft, luxurious pelts and should be handled gently. Part of their fur can be shed (so-called fur-slip) if they are handled roughly or the fur grasped too tightly. They are nocturnal and do not hibernate.

Table 1

Normal biological information

Adult weight	400 - 500 g, female larger than male
Birth weight	30 - 60 g
Litter size	1 - 5, usually 2
Gestation	111 days
Weaning age	6 - 8 weeks
Life-span	10 years (up to 18 years has been recorded)
Sexual maturity	8 months
Body temp	38 - 39°C
Pulse	100 - 150 per minute
Respiratory rate	40 - 80 per minute

ANATOMICAL FACTS

Like all rodents, the chinchilla's teeth grow continuously throughout life. They have a digestive tract (like other rodents and rabbits) that is specialised for digesting large amounts of fibre. Their breeding season is from November through to April or May and their young (like those of guinea pigs) are born with eyes open, fully furred and active.

SELECTION

Chinchillas are sold at pet shops, through breeders and at exotic pet shows. As with any pet purchase avoid chinchillas that appear ill. They should be bright and alert and move quickly when startled. Avoid pets with closed eyes or discharge from the eyes or nose. Check the ears for redness or excess wax which might indicate an infection. If possible, examine the teeth and make sure the incisors (front teeth) are not overgrown. The pet should feel neither fat nor thin; you should be able to feel the ribs with just a small amount of fat over them. Check the anal area for diarrhoea or moistness which might indicate a gastrointestinal infection.

Ideally the chinchilla should come with a health guarantee that may require a check-up by a veterinary surgeon within a few days (usually 48 hours). The first consultation will include determining the animal's weight and checking for lumps or bumps, dehydration or starvation. A faecal test will show if there are internal parasites and the veterinary surgeon can determine the sex. If all turns out well, the animal will be given a clean bill of health. At this initial examination the veterinary surgeon will also be able to advise owners of potential problems and help avoid them. Like all pets, chinchillas should be examined and have a faecal test annually. They do not require vaccinations.

FEEDING

Chinchillas should be given grass hay *ad libitum* (literally 'at pleasure' but meaning available 24 hours a day). While alfalfa hay can be used, it should not be the sole source of hay as it is too rich and can result in digestive disturbances. Additionally, a small amount (several tablespoons per day) of rabbit or chinchilla pellets can be given. Any necessary changes in diet should be made slowly, over several days, to decrease the chance of gastrointestinal problems. Chinchillas do not require additional vitamins or treats, although fresh vegetables and fruit should be offered regularly. Do not offer any 'human' food without checking first with a veterinary surgeon.

Fig. 1

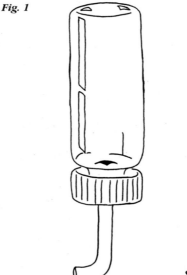

Sipper bottle

Water should be available 24 hours a day and most owners hang a sipper bottle in the cage. Check the bottle daily whenever changing the water to make sure the sipper tube has not become clogged with food.

HOUSING

A chinchilla cage should allow the animal a lot of movement. Multilevel cages work well. Like other rodents, chinchillas love to chew so wire-mesh cages are preferable to wooden ones. Many veterinary surgeons recommend covering at least part of the floor with safety glass or wood to lessen the pressure on the feet from a wire-bottomed cage. Newspaper or wood shavings can be placed over the wire mesh.

Chinchillas are very susceptible to heat stroke; environmental temperature should be kept below 26°C (80°F) and high humidity should be avoided. Most owners keep one or two pets in a cage and often the two are mates. Chinchillas are social animals that rarely fight but injury and death can occur from fighting. Care should be taken when introducing a new chinchilla into the resident pet's cage. If several chinchillas are wanted it is best to purchase them as youngsters.

To help them keep their teeth filed down put wood in the cage and possibly a chew toy, as long as the smallest piece of the toy is too big to be swallowed. Chinchillas have a unique grooming habit and it is important for them to have access to a dust bath. Each day they should be provided with a bath which is nine parts silver sand to one part Fuller's earth (available at most pet shops). Ensure that there is enough dust for the chinchilla to roll around in and remove the bath after use, keeping it clean and free of faeces and urine.

They enjoy soft towels as bedding but inspect the towels often to make sure they are not being chewed and swallowed (this could cause intestinal obstruction).

Cages should be cleaned weekly with soap and water (rinse well).

COMMON DISEASES and SPECIAL PROBLEMS

These include respiratory diseases, overgrown teeth, diarrhoea, heat stroke and bite wounds. The latter can be common when chinchillas are housed together. They can also occur in an attack by the household cat or dog (a large dog can kill a chinchilla). Bites by other chinchillas, dogs and cats are often infected with various bacteria and if left untreated the infection can spread throughout the body. Bites are a true medical emergency which require immediate veterinary help in the form of antibiotics (see antibiotic sensitivity, below) and thorough wound cleaning (anaesthesia may be necessary).

Signs of disease

Signs of disease in chinchillas may be specific for a certain disease but often are vague and non-specific, such as a chinchilla with anorexia (lack of appetite) and lethargy. These can be seen in many diseases including pneumonia, overgrown teeth, cancer and even kidney or liver failure. Any deviation from normal should be a cause for concern and requires immediate evaluation by a veterinary surgeon.

Antibiotic sensitivity

Rodents are very susceptible to antibiotic toxicity. Some antibiotics designed for human use, including penicillin and erythromycin, can be fatal to chinchillas. Owners should never use antibiotics in or on their pet rodents without first consulting a veterinary surgeon experienced in rodent medicine.

Dental disease

As in many rodents, overgrown teeth are common in chinchillas whose teeth grow continuously throughout life. Either the front teeth (incisors) or back teeth (molars) can overgrow. Signs of this include drooling (slobbering) and a depressed appetite. Eye problems such as weeping or discharge can also signal overgrown teeth. Overgrown incisors are easy to see upon inspecting the mouth but it is often difficult to tell if the molars are overgrown. Anaesthesia, to allow a thorough evaluation of the mouth, and radiographs (X-rays) may be needed. Overgrown teeth should be trimmed by a veterinary surgeon. In the past, nail clippers were used but, because of the chance of injuring jaws or teeth, a file with a rotating burr or a small rotating saw is now often used, with the chinchilla anaesthetised.

Diarrhoea

Diarrhoea is not a disease *per se* but rather a sign of disease. Rodents, whose digestive systems are designed to digest a large amount of fibre, easily develop diarrhoea due to changes in diet, incorrect use of antibiotics, stress and diets low in fibre or high in fat and protein. The cause is diagnosed after tests including microscopic faecal examinations, cultures, radiographs, blood tests and possibly exploratory surgery. Treatment depends on the cause: if it is parasites a deworming medication should be given, if bacteria then antibiotics and if inappropriate food the chinchilla should be placed on a high-fibre diet.

Fur slip

Chinchillas have the ability to release or 'slip' patches of fur when handled roughly, when stressed or when fighting. Usually there is no permanent damage and the fur regrows, although the new growth takes several months.

Heat stroke

Heat stroke, which can be a common problem in well-furred rodents, also occurs in chinchillas. Being normal inhabitants of the Andes mountains, they are very comfortable at 2-7°C (35-45°F). Temperatures above 26.6°C (80°F), especially with high humidity, can lead to fatal heat stroke. Signs of heat stroke are similar to those in any pet with this problem and include panting, high body temperature, open-mouth breathing and recumbency with reluctance to move.

Heat stroke requires urgent treatment. The chinchilla can be cooled with ice packs, cold water enemas, various medications, intraperitoneal fluids and intravenous fluid therapy. Chinchillas discovered with heat stroke at home should be cooled immediately: apply cold water and ice packs to the armpits, groin and neck. Owners should not give their pets medications such as aspirin or paracetamol.

Respiratory disease

Respiratory disease is relatively common in pet chinchillas and the problem can easily become a severe pneumonia. Conditions such as overcrowding, poor ventilation and high humidity may predispose to pneumonia. Common signs include lack of appetite, lethargy, difficulty breathing, nasal discharge and swollen lymph nodes. Again, the treatment includes antibiotics and chinchillas which are lethargic and have stopped eating require hospitalisation, possibly with fluid therapy and force feeding which can best be provided in a veterinary surgery with experience of caring for such rodents.

CHIPMUNKS

Chipmunks are members of the squirrel family and, while there are many different species inhabiting North America and Asia, most of those bought in British pet shops are Siberian (Latin name: *Tamias sibricus*). A few years ago almost all the chipmunks available were imported from Japan and Korea but now most animals are captive-bred. Being a diurnal rodent the chipmunk is active during the day and a well-designed enclosure can make life interesting and enjoyable for chipmunks and the humans keeping them!

Although chipmunks can be tamed and become friendly, they are still wild. This means that although you can handle them with care they are not cuddly and can bite extremely hard! To cope with living in captivity chipmunks need an environment which mimics as closely as possible their wild habitat. Chipmunks can live up to eight or nine years, although three to five is more usual. Females generally outlive males.

Table 2

Normal biological information

Adult weight	72 - 120 g
Adult length	head and body 12 - 19 cm, 11 cm tail
Litter size	3 - 5 but may vary from 1 - 10
Oestrous cycle	usually 13 - 14 days (range 11 - 21 days)
Gestation	31 - 32 days (range 28 - 35 days)
Emergence of young	about 35 days (range 28 - 35 days)
Weaning age	1 week after emergence
Life-span	male 2.7 years though some live to 8 - 9 years, in wild 8 years
Body temperature	38°C awake, few degrees above environmental temperature when hibernating
Respiratory rate	75 per minute approx. (resting)

FEEDING

In the wild chipmunks forage for a wide range of foodstuffs from fruits, nuts and green vegetables to carrion. Food in captivity should be as varied as possible in an attempt to mirror this natural diet. Giving nuts in their shells will encourage the wearing down of teeth and provide a good activity to prevent boredom. Providing hard wood to chew will also help.

HOUSING

In the wild chipmunks are mostly solitary, living in earth burrows or tree holes. They spend much of their time foraging for food over a wide area. If kept in a small cage they will develop stereotyped behaviour patterns which are as disturbing to watch as they must be for the rodents performing them. Chipmunks need as large an enclosure as you can provide, either outdoors with nestboxes for rest in dry and draught-free conditions or indoors, again with hideaways. They need plenty of branches to climb and opportunity to dig burrows, since this is a major activity in the wild.

Do be careful not to let chipmunks escape from the enclosure, as they can move extremely fast and it is illegal to release any non-indigenous species into the countryside. If animals are inside, ensure that they are well away from television sets as the high-pitched background noise, which is above our hearing threshold, can cause stress and even death to chipmunks.

BREEDING

Breeding chipmunks is not difficult and during the two breeding seasons, around March to April and September to October, females may have litters of up to ten young. The gestation period is about 30 days and the young leave the nest at about seven weeks old. While the female should not be disturbed during gestation and when the young are in the nest, she should be provided with plenty of food and water.

COMMON PROBLEMS

Dental disease

As the teeth of chipmunks, like those of other rodents and rabbits, grow continually, overgrowth is a common problem. As mentioned, this can be prevented by giving nuts in their shells and plenty of hard wood to chew.

Pneumonia

Pneumonia can develop if animals are kept in a draughty outside enclosure. Ensure that nest boxes and rest areas are draught-free and dry.

Stress

Stress can occur if chipmunks are kept in close confinement. They are essentially solitary, so over-crowding them will cause problems, especially if one particularly aggressive male dominates the group.

FERRETS

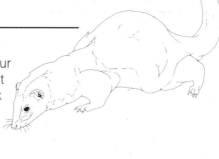

Ferrets come in several different colour schemes. The polecat ferret, the most popular, has a buff-coloured coat with black markings on the face, feet and tail. Albino ferrets are white with pink eyes and others have a buff coat with light markings.

The female is called a jill, the male a hob and the infants are kits.

Table 3

Normal biological information

Adult weight	male 700 - 2000 g; female 600 - 900 g
Birth weight	5 - 15 g
Litter size	5 - 13 (average 8)
Gestation	38 - 44 days (average 42)
Weaning age	6 - 8 weeks
Weaning weight	300 - 500 g
Life-span	5 - 11 years
Sexual maturity	5 - 9 months
Rectal temperature	38.6°C (range 37.8- 40.0°C)
Heart rate	300 - 400 per minute
Respiratory rate	30 - 40 per minute

SELECTION

Ferrets can make good pets but they can be aggressive and bite. They are excellent escape artists and can squeeze through the tiniest openings and cracks. Homes must be 'ferret-proofed' to prevent escape and injury. They are naturally inquisitive and will chew and swallow many things. It is highly recommended that owners put a collar with a bell on a ferret so that he/she can be found easily (make sure the bell can't be swallowed if it becomes detached, or ensure it is so firmly secured to the collar that it cannot come loose). Never let a ferret out of your sight when he is out of his cage. If you leave the room, even for a minute, take him with you or put him back in the cage or carrier.

Ferrets can be purchased in pet shops, from breeders or ferret club members. Look for a young ferret, ideally. The eyes and nose should be clear and free of any discharge that might indicate a respiratory infection (or distemper). The ferret should be curious and inquisitive; it should not be thin and emaciated. If possible, examine the mouth for broken teeth, discoloured gums (they should be light pink), or obvious sores, any of which suggest disease. Check for wetness around the anus, which might indicate diarrhoea and for external parasites such as fleas. Ask if the ferret has been spayed or neutered or de-scented.

Rubber toys are not safe for ferrets, as they often chew off and swallow small pieces! Diagnosis of an obstruction is often difficult in a ferret; usually the problem is solved during surgery but is often fatal if not treated early. Hard toys or dog chews are safe, as are rawhide treats in small amounts. Other safe toys include ping pong and golf balls, small cans, cardboard tubes and very hard plastic toys. A cloth toy is all right as long as the ferret is not chewing off pieces of it!

Ferrets may be spayed or neutered and even sometimes de-scented. Unless you want to breed your prospective pet, sterilisation is preferred. Intact (un-neutered) male ferrets have a musky odour and can be aggressive; female ferrets have problems with persistent heat unless bred (common diseases and special problems, see below).

The anal sacs of ferrets can secrete a foul-smelling liquid, thus some people consider de-scented ferrets (which can have these sacs removed at the time of spaying or neutering when 8-12 weeks) make better pets. Others feel this is part of being a normal hob and should be expected. Even after de-scenting ferrets have a slightly musky odour. They can be bathed weekly or every other week with a gentle moisturising shampoo recommended by a veterinary surgeon. Ferrets should also have their sharp claws trimmed regularly (ask the vet for instructions).

Just like dogs and cats, ferrets require a series of vaccinations as youngsters. They should be vaccinated against canine distemper at eight, 12 and 16 weeks of age. Once a year they require an examination, a faecal test for internal parasites and vaccination boosters. Once a ferret becomes five years old a complete geriatric work-up is recommended by some veterinary surgeons for the early detection of problems common in older ferrets, such as heart disease and cancer.

Ferrets, like many small mammals, are extremely susceptible to heat stress or stroke. The ambient temperature must be kept below 26°C (80°F).

Within 48 hours of bringing home a new ferret, he/she should be examined by a veterinary surgeon, ideally one experienced in treating ferrets. The vet will discuss proper diet, housing and toys. A vaccination program will be set up and a faecal sample checked for worms. At this initial examination the veterinary surgeon will also be able to advise owners of potential problems and help avoid them (see below). Like dogs and cats, ferrets require annual veterinary visits.

FEEDING

Ferret food or one of the many brands of cat food available can be fed. Additionally, you have the choice of wet, dry or semi-moist foods. Any of these diets will be enjoyed by the ferret. Keep in mind that a pet 'is what he eats', so advise owners to provide the best food possible. A ferret needs a full animal protein diet so dog food or a vegetarian diet is not appropriate.

Many consider that ferrets should have food available 24 hours a day. If they are eating a high-quality diet, extra vitamins are not essential. However, there are several brands of very palatable vitamins that can be offered as a low-fat treat. While obesity is uncommon in ferrets, they can become overweight if fed a lot of high-calorie treats. Be sure to check with a vet before giving any 'human' food. Crisps, biscuits or sweets should not be given; they can contribute to upset stomach, pancreatitis, obesity and, in some instances (chocolate), can be fatal!

Fig. 2

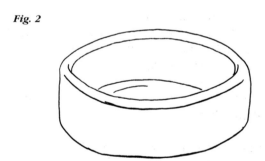

Fresh water in a ceramic dish that will not
easily tip over should be available at all times

HOUSING

Ferrets, who have a well-deserved reputation as curious creatures and escape artists, should be housed in a cage which is securely closed and locked. Inside you can place a litterbox, towels for bedding and burrowing and perhaps a container such as a shoe box. Ferrets can learn to use a litterbox.

Food and water bowls are often left in the cage. Since ferrets are naturally playful, it is common for them to spill their food and water. You might try using heavy ceramic dishes to prevent this, or a holder for the bowls that attaches them to the cage. Some owners construct a multi-level 'apartment' for their pets; this can be done with wood or cardboard, as long as the ferrets do not chew and swallow the 'flooring'. It is critical to keep their house at or below 80°F (26°C) and well ventilated.

BREEDING

The gestation period is about 42 days (compared with 60 for dogs and cats and 270 for humans). Like puppies and kittens, kits are born deaf and with their eyes closed. They begin walking by about three weeks of age, which is also when their eyes and ears open. By about six weeks they can be weaned onto kitten or ferret food. The average lifespan is five to eleven years; and some vets consider them middle aged at four and geriatric by six.

COMMON DISEASES AND SPECIAL PROBLEMS

Ferrets have several unique problems: during a physical examination, for instance the veterinary surgeon may find an enlarged spleen, especially in an older pet. While not a sign of any one disease, spleen enlargement indicates the need for further investigation. It could be due to inflammation of the spleen, malignant tumour or heart disease. Occasionally, diagnostic tests are negative for a specific disease, in which case the diagnosis will be 'benign hypersplenism' or 'benign splenomegaly'.

Signs of disease

These may be specific for a certain disease but most commonly they are vague and non-specific, such as a ferret with anorexia (lack of appetite) and lethargy. These can occur with many diseases including intestinal foreign bodies, various causes of diarrhoea and many types of cancer. Loss of appetite and lethargy indicate a guarded prognosis and the need for intensive care which can include fluid therapy and force feeding, but any deviation from normal should be a cause for concern and requires immediate evaluation by a vet.

Cancer

More so than dogs and cats, ferrets contract cancer quite readily and early in life. Since early detection is critical to survival, many vets suggest that every ferret five years of age and older should have a geriatric screening annually. This screening includes a complete blood count and biochemistry profile, radiographs (X-rays) of the chest and abdomen, urinalysis and an ECG (electrocardiogram). Several types of cancer are common including cancer of the pancreas (called an insulinoma), adrenal gland (often seen in conjunction with the insulinoma), and lymph nodes and white blood cells (lymphosarcoma). The various cancers can be treated surgically, medically or with a combination of both depending on the type. Any lump or bump should therefore be investigated immediately by a veterinary surgeon as many types of cancer can be cured if diagnosed early.

Canine distemper/human influenza

Ferrets can contract the dog distemper virus and the human 'flu virus. As in the dog, distemper can be fatal and they should be vaccinated against this disease. Clinical signs include loss of appetite, a thick eye and/or nasal discharge and often a rash on the chin, abdomen or groin. Treatment is supportive and should be attempted as the disease mimics human influenza in ferrets. The difference is that with distemper the ferret will be dead within one-two weeks and with 'flu he/she should be better in that time. The signs of 'flu are similar to those in people. Treatment consists of antibiotics and decongestants. Occasionally fluid therapy or force feeding will be needed. Never give a ferret any over-the-counter or prescription drugs without checking with a veterinary surgeon.

Diarrhoea

Diarrhoea is not a disease *per se*, but rather a sign of a gastrointestinal problem. In ferrets several conditions can result in diarrhoea including internal parasites. *Helicobacter musteli* is a spirochete-type bacterium that causes ulcers and diarrhoea in ferrets; similar spirochetes cause stomach ulcers in people and dogs. Proliferative colitis is caused by a *Campylobacter* bacterium and is treated with antibiotics.

Diarrhoea can be treated with several different medications depending upon the cause. Intestinal parasites require the appropriate deworming medication, infections are treated with antibiotics and occasionally anti-ulcer medication. Owners should avoid home treatment without a proper diagnosis as many diseases appear similar and mimic each other. Intestinal foreign bodies usually require immediate surgery. Since signs of a foreign body are very similar to those of parasites and infection, early diagnosis is important.

Foreign bodies

Intestinal foreign bodies are a common problem in ferrets, especially those less than one year old. Being curious creatures, ferrets commonly investigate, chew and swallow many objects, most commonly rubber parts of shoes, furniture and mattress stuffing, rubber bands, pencil rubbers and parts of dog and cat toys. These obstructions are difficult to diagnose unless the owner sees the ferret swallowing the object or knows a piece of the object is missing. They are hard to identify on routine radiographs (X-rays). Common signs are the same as with many ferret diseases and include lack of appetite, vomiting, lethargy, diarrhoea and gradual body wasting. Vomiting of a severe, projectile nature suggests a complete obstruction.

Parasites

Like dogs and cats, ferrets can contract various intestinal parasites as well as external ones. Yearly microscopic faecal examinations will allow easy diagnosis and treatment. External parasites, such as fleas, ticks, mange and ear mites, can also infect ferrets.

Heat stroke

Ferrets are very susceptible to extreme heat so their environmental temperature should be kept below 26°C (80° F). Just like dogs and cats, ferrets do not sweat. Heat stroke is manifested by open-mouth breathing and an elevated rectal temperature (normal temperature is between 37.7° and 38.8°C (100-104°F); average is about the same as dogs and cats 38°C (101.5°F). Heat stroke is a true emergency. First aid involves cooling the ferret by running cold water over its body or fanning it to reduce its temperature. Be careful not to chill the ferret. If shivering occurs stop the cooling process. After a few minutes of attempted cooling the ferret should be rushed to a vet who may use cold water enemas or cold fluids instilled into the abdomen to continue the cooling. Hospitalisation is required to monitor vital signs.

Persistent oestrus

Female ferrets continue in heat unless they are mated. The high levels of oestrogen in heat lead to aplastic anaemia (a gradual loss of production of red blood cells - and often white blood cells and platelets - in the bone marrow). This is not seen in spayed jills.

Signs of aplastic anaemia include lethargy and pale mucous membranes in a female intact ferret that is obviously in heat (manifested by a swollen vulva - the outer lips of the female reproductive tract). Treatment includes hormonal therapy to bring her out of heat, antibiotics, iron, vitamins and often blood transfusions. Ferrets do not appear to have any identifiable blood types; if needed, blood from a dog or preferably a cat can be given. They are very susceptible to hypoglycaemia (low blood sugar) and for this reason they are fasted for only a few hours (rather than overnight) before surgery. After stabilisation the jill can be spayed. An extremely anaemic ferret is usually beyond help and euthanasia is recommended. Aplastic anaemia is very serious and often expensive to treat. Any female ferret that will not be bred at every heat cycle should be spayed by 4-6 months of age. An alternative is to use a vasectomised hob to mate the jill.

Ringworm

Ringworm is an occasional infection in ferrets and usually manifests as a circular area of hair loss with slight scaliness around the periphery of the circle. Diagnosis can be accurate only with a special culture of the skin, scales and hair. It can be transmitted to other pets and to people, so care should be used in handling infected animals.

Ringworm can be treated much the same as it is in dogs and cats and involves medicated shampooing, topical medications and oral medication for severe infections. Mild cases often respond to topical therapy alone. Ringworm appears similar to other skin conditions so correct diagnosis is important before treatment starts.

GERBILS

These interesting animals have needs similar to most other captive rodents and the chapters on hamsters, mice and rats contain much general information which will help the gerbil-owner (but note that the diet of the guinea pig is substantially different). Gerbils are desert animals and drink very little water but, like other rodents, their water should be fresh every day. If supplying a water bottle with a sipper tube, check often that the end of the tube does not become clogged with food (effectively leaving the pet without water). This low water intake means they urinate only small amounts.

Table 4

Normal biological information

Adult weight	50 - 60 g, male greater than female
Litter size	4 - 6
Gestation	24 - 26 days (up to 42 days if delayed implantation)
Duration of oestrus	4 - 6 days
Life-span	3 - 5 yrs - female longer than male
Sexual maturity	10 weeks
Rectal temperature	37.4° - 39.0°C
Respiratory rate	90 - 140 per minute

HOUSING

Unlike hamsters, gerbils are animals which can usually be housed in groups, although this does bring the attendant risk of a population explosion unless a group of females are housed together.

COMMON PROBLEMS

Gerbils have high blood cholesterol and lipid (fat) levels but, interestingly, do not generally show signs of heart disease or atherosclerosis. They are unique among rodents in that many of them have mild spontaneous fits (epilepsy), often after being handled or startled. Medication to control these fits is not usually needed.

Fig. 3

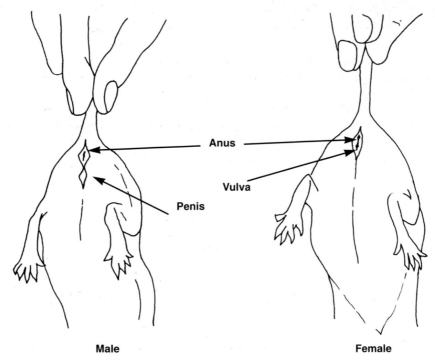

Male   **Female**

External genitalia of adult gerbil

Note the longer ano-genital distance in the male.

Dermatitis

Sometimes gerbils suffer from dermatitis, particularly on the muzzle. This can be caused by infection with either the bacterium *Staphylococcus* or a mite (mange), or by the pet constantly rubbing its snout on the feeders or the cage. The infections are often difficult to tell apart as both cause areas of hair loss (alopecia) and moisture but, once diagnosed, antibiotic treatment can be started.

Endocrine problems

Gerbils appear particularly prone to diabetes, Cushing's disease and obesity. Interestingly they readily develop very high levels of cholesterol in their blood even on low fat diets but do not seem particularly prone to heart disease.

Epilepsy

This can be quite common in some gerbils ranging from mild attacks to severe fits. These may be precipitated by handling or changes in light levels. Generally owners are more concerned than the animals!

GUINEA PIGS

Guinea pigs originated in South America but were probably introduced into Europe soon after the first Spanish explorers returned from that continent in the 1500s. Even though they came from a tropical area these rodents proved to be hardy and adapted to temperate climates such as that of Britain. They became favourite pets in the early part of this century and are also bred as show animals, with a wide variety of coat colours and fur types.

Table 5

Normal biological information

Adult weight	750 - 1000 g.
Litter size	1 - 6 (average 2 - 4)
Gestation	59 - 72 days (depending on litter size)
Weaning age	3 weeks
Life-span	4 - 8 years
Sexual maturity	male 9 - 12 weeks, female 4-6 weeks
Rectal temperature	38.6° (37.2° - 39.5°C)
Heart rate	130 - 190 per minute
Respiratory rate	90 - 150 per minute

FEEDING

Guinea pigs are herbivores rather like rabbits although the physiology of the gastrointestinal system is less well understood than that of the rabbit. The critical area of the guinea pig diet is the requirement for vitamin C. Apart from that, the key to a healthy diet is variety. Imagine what the guinea pig has to eat in its native environment of the South American forests: a bit of everything from fruits through greens to root vegetables. People may feed a dry guinea pig mix with few fresh vegetables and expect that to satisfy the animal's requirements. It does not.

Vitamin C

For every animal there is a set of essential nutrients and another set of non-essential ones. Animals need a regular dietary supply of essential ingredients, while they can produce their own supply of the non-essentials. These essential elements differ between species so that, for instance, the cat and ferret require a regular supply of the amino acid taurine while other mammals like ourselves produce taurine by metabolising other amino acids. In the guinea pig and man one key essential nutrient is vitamin C. The vast majority of other animals produce their own vitamin C from their intestinal bacterial flora but for some reason guinea pigs and humans are not able to do so - this is why the eighteenth century sailors developed scurvy when not able to eat fresh fruit. Vitamin C is vital in the normal development and maintenance of skin and mucosal surfaces like gums. It is also important in the healing of wounds to these structures. As well as predisposing to skin problems, a lack of vitamin C seems to make the body more prone to other diseases, infections and poor condition. A guinea pig which is reluctant to walk, has swollen feet or haemorrhages/ulcers on its gums or elsewhere is likely to be deficient in vitamin C.

There is no reason why a guinea pig should be deficient in this nutrient, since it is available from fresh fruit and green vegetables but it is a relatively unstable compound. If only a dry mix with old hay is given, most of the vitamin C will have decomposed by oxidization. If a guinea pig develops a deficiency, it is much better to give a crushed tablet by mouth rather than in drinking water, since the vitamin breaks down rapidly in water and loses its potency. To ensure vitamin C in the diet feed broccoli, which has a very high level of the vitamin.

Given that guinea pigs are adapted to a diet of fibrous vegetable matter, good-quality hay is important, with commercial guinea pig pellets forming the bulk of the food. A mix like this will keep the pet happy and healthy.

A guinea pig should be picked up with one hand around the shoulders and the other supporting its rear end

HOUSING

A large variety of hutches and cages are used for guinea pigs. They can be kept outside in the summer and a good draught-free but well ventilated mobile run on the grass is very acceptable as long as there is also a dry covered area. Pens should be at least 30 cm (12 inches) high to avoid escapes and should be covered with mesh to keep cats out. Indoor cages in the winter should allow at least 0.2 square metres of floor space per guinea pig. Since they are social animals guinea pigs can be kept in small to medium groups but clearly mating will increase the number of animals so single-sex groups are advisable. Sometimes they fight when first put together but they should be left to sort out their 'pecking order', which might take a couple of days. They may continue to squeak at one

Fig. 5

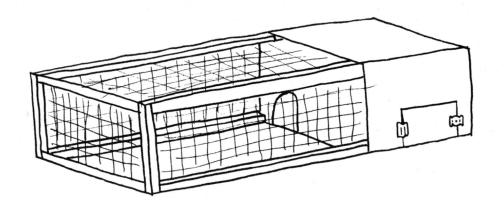

Guinea pig run

(also suitable for rabbits)

another intermittently and appear to be aggressive but do not worry - they are just re-establishing the hierarchy. They rarely bite (one of the reasons they make good pets) but be prepared for them to squeal when handled. Temperatures between 12° and 20°C (about 52°- 68°F) are ideal. Anything over 27°C (approx. 82°F) will lead to heat-stroke, especially in animals that are overweight or pregnant.

BREEDING

Guinea pigs are one of a group of rodents called the hystricomorphs with an unusual reproductive physiology and breeding strategy. Chinchillas also belong to this group and others, like the plains vichaca, are not kept in captivity so will not worry us here! Guinea pigs mature at around three months but should not be used for breeding for another three months. After about eight months of age the female guinea pig's pelvic bones become more tightly fused and, if she has not had a litter by that time, producing young can be more difficult. Why does this problem exist since most species can delay giving birth until they are older? The difference with the guinea pig is that she does not have a large litter of tiny immature young (as the rat or mouse does), but between two and four fully-developed well-furred offspring. The average gestation period is 63 days. These large babies have a hard time getting through the pelvic canal unless the mother's pelvic bones are relatively immature and malleable. Large offspring also predispose the mother to pregnancy toxaemia, a metabolic disorder resulting in low blood calcium and high blood pressure. It manifests as loss of appetite in the early stages, deteriorating to muscle twitching and coma. Prompt veterinary

Fig. 6

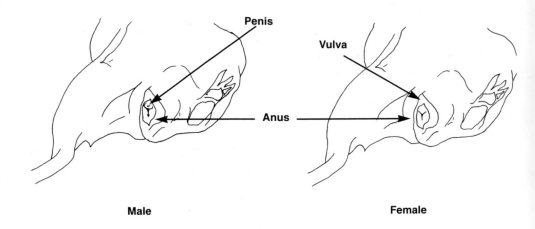

External genitalia of adult guinea pig

attention can save animals but the problem can be reduced to a minimum by providing plenty of water and green foods during pregnancy, as throughout life.

There is a relatively high incidence of dead babies in the normal guinea pig and if the gestation should continue over 70 days it is likely the litter will be born dead. Interestingly the guinea pig, along with other hystricomorph rodents, starts off with a much larger set of foetuses in her uterus but many of them die before birth, many very early on but some late in gestation or even at birth. The reason is unclear but it may be a mechanism of producing the maximum number of babies for a limited and varying food supply.

As with many rodents, the female guinea pig will be able to mate within a few hours of giving birth. She should not be allowed to, however, since it is much better that she has time to replenish her metabolic reserves before becoming pregnant again. If a guinea pig has a large litter of over three or four piglets it is worth fostering some onto another sow since, unlike other rodents, she has only one pair of mammary glands to suckle her offspring.

HAMSTERS

These small rodents can be found in the wild in Eastern Europe, the Middle East, North Africa, China and Siberia. All the golden hamsters in captivity in Britain are said to be descended from one male and two females imported from Syria in 1931. A wide variety of coat colours is available and long-haired varieties and a number of different species are becoming more common, for example the Chinese hamster (*Cricetulus griseus*), the Russian hamster (*Phodopus sungorus*) and the common golden or Syrian hamster (*Mesocricetus auratus*).

Table 6

Normal biological information

Adult weight	male 85 - 140 g, female 95 - 120 g
Birth weight	2 - 5 g
Litter size	4 - 12
Gestation	15 - 18 days (21 days for Chinese hamster)
Weaning age	21 days
Life-span	2 - 3 yrs
Sexual maturity	male 6-8 weeks, female 4 weeks (Chinese 14 weeks)
Rectal temperature	36.2 - 37.5°C
Respiratory rate	74 (40 - 130) per minute

The hamster is in some ways a good pet, having simple housing needs and being relatively odourless. It is however predominantly nocturnal and thus not a great pet for children. These animals often have to be kept alone as they fight when housed together and can inflict a considerable bite if a human picks them up incorrectly. However, hamsters kept together from an early age will not fight but rather mate and give rise to a population explosion!

The black dot on each hip, more developed in the male than the female, is a gland used for territorial marking. Both sexes have cheek pouches on the inside of the mouth, in which food and even baby hamsters can be stored temporarily. These rodents can hibernate so, because they are the most aggressive of the so-called 'pocket pets', they should be awakened carefully. One that appears dead may be merely in a torpor and should be warmed and awakened, not buried!

Fig. 7

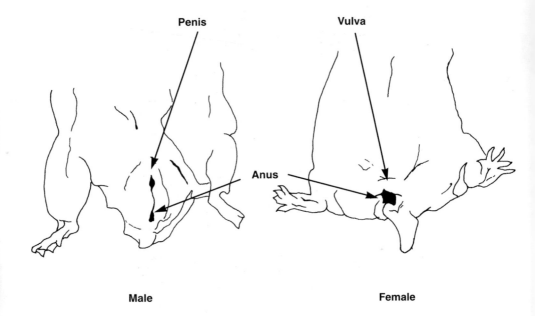

Penis   Vulva

Anus

Male   Female

External genitalia of adult hamsters

Note the longer ano-genital distance in the male.

HANDLING

Hamsters are best picked up by encouraging them to walk into cupped hands. Startling them will result in a bite which is more the fault of the handler than the handled!

FEEDING

Hamsters should be fed predominantly on commercial rodent mixes. Too often owners give too much vegetable matter and high-energy sunflower seeds. Remember that these animals are used to a fairly dry environment without many green vegetables in their diet. Supplementation with seeds, grains, fruit and greens is useful but these foods should not be given in excess resulting in an unbalanced diet. Water should always be available.

Fig. 8

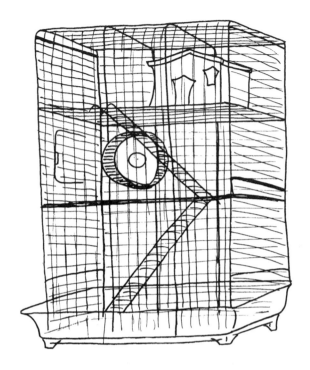

Hamster cage

Note different levels and 'hiding' home.
Wheel also included which should be solid.

HOUSING

A captive environment needs to offer space and exercise facility plus privacy and warmth. Cages should be escape-proof and gnaw-resistant and plastic or polypropylene cages are excellent. Metal is not particularly warm and comfortable while wood is not gnaw-proof and is difficult to sterilise.

Hamsters need plenty of bedding which absorbs moisture. Sawdust or wood chippings can be used and peat is an alternative. Cotton wool should be avoided as it can cause severe constipation and any strands of material, artificial or natural, can wind around legs causing restricted blood flow.

COMMON PROBLEMS

Dental disease

As with all rodents, hamsters' teeth grow continually and have to be worn down all the time. When there is malocclusion (teeth do not grind together satisfactorily) there will be severe problems of teeth overgrowing. This causes gum ulceration, subsequent pain and failure to eat adequately.

Hair loss

Hair loss, scratching and red skin may be related to a mite called Demodex or to a fungus, ringworm. Both can be diagnosed by a skin and hair sample examined under the microscope and there are effective treatments for them.

Parasites

In hamsters a gut parasite (*Hymenolepis nana*) is a significant problem and can lead to intestinal obstruction. It can be treated by a veterinary surgeon, as can pinworms, although many consider the latter are not a clinical problem in hamsters.

Respiratory diseases

As with other rodents, respiratory disease is common and can be caused by viruses or bacteria. Hamsters are kept singly by most owners so the sort of respiratory problems seen in big colonies of mice and rats are less likely.

Wet tail

The most common problem in hamsters is wet tail (proliferative ileitis or transmissible ileal hyperplasia). The causes are unclear and various bacteria can be isolated from animals with the disease, which can be transmitted by direct contact. However there are probably many factors which predispose to the condition. The small intestine in these cases is thickened, which may cause the signs resulting in death in the early stages of the disease but also just when the animal seems to be recovering. Treatment with antibiotics works only rarely and the vital factor is supportive therapy: fluids by mouth to resolve the dehydration in these small animals with fairly rampant diarrhoea. Antibiotics can themselves cause intestinal upset and should not be given by mouth if at all possible.

MICE

Mice are kept for many reasons, from being children's pets to prize show animals. They are not ideal pets in many ways but are easy to keep in captivity. Most captive mice in this country are of the species *Mus musculus* although the dark brown or sandy-coloured deer mouse (*Peromyscus leucopus*) is also kept. The harvest mouse (*Micromys minutus*) and the long-tailed field mouse (*Apodemus sylvaticus*) are also occasionally kept.

Most mice sold as children's pets are white although many other colour variants are possible. 'Selfs' have one body colour which may be black, blue, chocolate, fawn etc. 'Tans' have one colour on the upper body and are tan underneath. 'Marked' animals are white mice with a variety of colour patterns. The final group is the broadly-named AOV (any other variety). These include coat markings such as agouti, chinchilla and long-haired. If an owner wants to breed and show mice The National Mouse Club (see useful addresses) will provide all the information needed.

Table 7

Normal biological information

Adult weight	20 - 40 g
Litter size	8 - 12 (average 10)
Gestation	19 - 21 days
Weaning age	3 - 4 weeks
Life-span	2 - 3 years
Sexual maturity	6 - 7 weeks
Rectal temperature	37.5°C
Heart rate	500 - 600 per minute
Respiratory rate	100 - 250 per minute

HANDLING

Although mice are generally amenable to handling they should always be handled with care. Using your cupped hands is the best way to pick them up. Alternatively, a mouse can be lifted from its cage with one hand on the scruff of its neck and the other holding the tail base. Vets sometimes hold mice by the scruff to be able to examine them and give medication.

Fig. 9

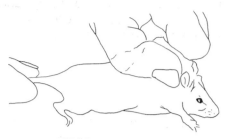

Picking up a mouse

A mouse should be lifted from its cage with one hand on the scruff of its neck and the other holding the tail base.

FEEDING

Mice can be fed a commercial complete ration supplemented with fruit and vegetables. They are happy to eat tit bits and chocolate but, while these can be useful in firming the owner-pet bond, they can lead to obesity and considerable health problems. The front teeth (incisors) grow continuously so pieces of hard wood or chewing devices can be provided to help keep the incisors in check. If they become overgrown the vet can trim them under anaesthesia with a rotating burr. In the past, nail clippers or wire cutters were used without anaesthesia, but these sometimes caused broken teeth, leading to more problems. Overgrown molars (back teeth) usually require anaesthesia and radiography before trimming.

HOUSING

Mice can be housed successfully in commercial or home-built cages. When making a cage it is vital that the owner remembers that mice can chew through wood or plastic very easily and, once free, will gnaw everything from household items to electrical cables. Metal and glass are good materials from which to build cages, which often include a separate bedding area although, given sufficient floor space, this is not necessary. The problem with most cages is that they are too small. A space 50 x 40 cm (20 x 16 inches) with a height of 25 cm (ten inches) will cater for three or four mice but the bigger the better. Wire mesh should be fine enough to prevent escape of young mice but sturdy enough to resist the teeth of adults. Any exercise wheel should be chosen carefully to avoid leg injuries or fractures. Only solid-bottom wheels should be used.

Bedding of either tissue paper or soft wood shavings needs regular cleaning. This is a good reason for a hard plastic base to the cage, which should be sterilised regularly. Do not use the fine bedding or nesting material available in pet shops since, as described below, a thread can act as a torniquet and lead to loss of limbs.

Mice should be housed at 14-26°C (60-80°F) and never above 30°C (86°F), when they can die of heat stroke.

Male mice are usually housed alone. Females rarely fight and are often housed together. Newly-assembled male groups, new males entering established territories, and mice previously housed alone are more likely to fight. Never house different species together (e.g. rats and mice).

BREEDING

Adult mice can most easily be sexed when one of either sex is available for comparison. The anus and vulva in the female are much closer together than the anus and penis in the male. Mice are sexually mature at six to seven weeks and have a gestation of 19 to 21 days with a litter size of eight to 12. Weaning age is three to four weeks. Population explosions are a common problem and ideally mice should be kept in single-sex groups, the females being easier to manage than the males, who will fight, giving each other severe bites which may become infected. If a pair of mice are housed together they should be separated before the birth of young because within 12 hours they will mate, giving a very rapid increase in the pet population!

COMMON PROBLEMS

A mouse's lifespan is only two to three years so ageing changes and natural fatal conditions such as tumours are fairly common. If owners can recognise common changes they will know when to take their pet to a veterinary surgeon. Some people think it is not worth taking a mouse to the vet but those with mice as pets or show animals can become very attached to them. Remember that prolonging a mouse's life by several months with treatment can add a substantial fraction to their lifespan.

Antibiotic toxicities

All pet rodents are sensitive to certain antibiotics. Several of these antibiotics can be fatal; this is true whether the antibiotics are given orally, by injection or topically (on the skin) but is particularly the case in antibiotics given by mouth which upset the normal bacteria found in the gut of the rodent. Examples of toxic antibiotics include penicillin and related drugs, bacitracin, erythromycin, lincomycin, tylosin and streptomycin. Owners should never use antibiotics in or on their pet rodents without first consulting a veterinary surgeon experienced in rodent medicine.

Diarrhoea

Diarrhoea is common and can be caused by a wide range of infectious organisms. These range from bacteria, through single-celled organisms like coccidia to parasites, such as tapeworms. Among the bacteria are two of particular importance: *Salmonella* species and *Bacillus piliformis* . Salmonella is zoonotic (can be passed from animals to man) so any diarrhoea should be investigated with a faecal culture. An animal with salmonella may have to be put down but other bacteria can be treated with a drop of an antibiotic (such as neomycin or enrofloxaein) by mouth. *Bacillus piliformis* causes Tyzzer's disease which often results in generalised illness and death. Antibiotic treatment may be effective but also has severe side effects so should be used with caution (see antibiotic toxicities). With regard to prevention of infectious problems it is important to have a quarantine period for new animals coming into a collection.

Foot necrosis/gangrene

This can occur if a thread from unsuitable bedding becomes wound around a foot or a toe. Fine bedding or nesting material available in pet shops should not be used. The pets play with the material, the fine thread gets wrapped around a toe, foot or leg and within hours the body part is swelling and turning red. If not caught immediately, the swelling progresses to death (*necrosis*) of the limb followed shortly by gangrene. Amputation might be curative but often the cost of surgery forces owners to choose euthanasia for these pets.

Mammary tumours

Amazingly, breast tissue covers much of the body so cancer of the mammary glands (which is very common) can appear as a lump on the back. It is almost always malignant so the prognosis is very poor. Nevertheless tumours can be removed surgically and (as mentioned above) even a couple of months of extra life is significant. Other types of tumour, for example in the abdomen, can often be removed but the procedure is more difficult than removal of an external growth.

Pneumonia

Pneumonia is common and occurs more often in larger colonies of mice rather than in animals kept individually or in small groups. Animals with breathing difficulties, a hunched up posture and loss of general condition may have respiratory problems caused by viruses, bacteria or mycoplasma. These agents are more likely to flourish if mice are kept on dusty bedding or dirty flooring which holds ammonia from the pets' urine.

Ringworm

The skin fungus ringworm is common in mice. This should not be confused with barbering which happens when mice gnaw each other's fur and cause bald, often symmetrical patches. Notice that in a group of rodents there will be one, the dominant animal, which is not barbered. A vet will diagnose ringworm either by using an ultraviolet light, under which the ringworm lesions on the skin fluoresce, or by taking a small amount of hair and examining it under the microscope. This will also show if there are any fur mites causing the skin problem. Ringworm can be treated with medication (griseofulvin) by mouth; mites can be treated with an injection of ivermectin.

Sialodacryoadenitis (red tears)

Red tears, often seen in mice and rats, can result from viral or bacterial disease or stress. Often it is hard to tell what is causing the problem which looks as if blood is coming from the eyes. In the viral infection, usually the salivary and Harderian glands (those at the inner corner of the eye) are involved. Because rodents have porphyrins (pigments) in their tears, any discharge will be seen as red. Treatment is symptomatic and involves topical eye medication.

RABBITS

Rabbits make a good alternative to a dog or cat. Normally they are not aggressive, do not have to be walked and usually can be trained to use a litterbox. Rabbits are the third most common pet seen by veterinary surgeons after dogs and cats. Their average lifespan is eight to twelve years and they can breed at six months. Early spaying or neutering (at four to six months) is recommended to decrease medical and behavioural problems. In rabbits, known for their breeding ability, pregnancy lasts about 30 days and the litter is four to twelve bunnies, with an average of seven.

The animal's large ears help give it excellent hearing and a way to regulate body temperature: the skin over the ears is thin, with large blood vessels just below the surface so that blood flowing through the ears is affected by the ambient temperature very quickly. The rabbit raises its ears to lose heat and clamps them to its body to limit heat loss. The large veins of the ears are often the site of drawing blood for diagnostic testing. The alimentary canal has adapted for digesting the large amount of fibre a rabbit ingests in the wild and there are two pairs of upper incisor teeth. Rabbit teeth, like those of rodents, grow throughout life and may need periodic trimming by a vet. This can generally be avoided if rabbits are given blocks of wood to chew. Overgrown incisors may cause excessive drooling or the rabbit might stop eating but regular mouth checks should reveal the problem before symptoms occur.

Table 8

Normal biological information

Adult weight	1 - 8 kg (varies with breed and sex)
Litter size	4 - 12 (average 7)
Gestation	30 - 33 days
Weaning age	7 - 8 weeks
Life-span	8 - 12 yrs
Sexual maturity	16 - 24 weeks
Rectal temperature	38.3° (range 37.0° - 39.4° C)
Heart rate	220 per minute
Respiratory rate	35 - 60 per minute

SELECTION

When selecting a rabbit (either at a pet shop or from a breeder) it should, ideally, be a young one. Its eyes and nose should be clear of any discharge that might indicate a respiratory infection and it should be inquisitive. He/she should not be thin and emaciated. Check for fleas and ear mites (mites cause a waxy black exudate in the ears). If possible, examine the rabbit's mouth for broken or overgrown incisors (front teeth), discoloured gums (they should be light pink) and any obvious sores. Check for wetness around the anus (which could indicate diarrhoea) and ask if the rabbit has been spayed or neutered; most have not been at the time of purchase. These operations should ideally be performed by four to six months of age. Finally inquire if the seller is offering any guarantee of the rabbit's health.

The rabbit should be examined within 48 hours of purchase by a veterinary surgeon ideally one with a particular interest in these animals. He/she should discuss housing, proper diet and appropriate toys for the rabbit. A faecal sample should be examined for parasites and this should be repeated annually, with a physical examination. At this initial examination the veterinary surgeon will also be able to advise owners of potential problems.

Rabbits can and should be vaccinated against myxomatosis and haemorrhagic viral hepatitis (transmitted by insects and fleas).

HANDLING

Proper handling is important: the rabbit has a very light skeleton in relation to the rest of its body, therefore its bones break easily. Despite this lightweight frame the powerful back legs allow it to kick with great force. If a rabbit kicks while being held incorrectly it might break its back and become paralysed, requiring euthanasia. When carrying a rabbit always support its rear end. If it struggles put it on the ground immediately, give it time to quieten down and pick it up a few minutes later. Never pick it up by the ears. Ask a veterinary surgeon to show you the correct way to carry and restrain a rabbit.

Fig. 10

Picking up a rabbit

Note that the rabbit is grasped in one hand by the scruff of its neck and its weight supported by the other hand under its hind-quarters.

FEEDING

Adult rabbits should be given high-quality rabbit chow, pellets and good-quality hay, grass or clover. Up to a year old, pellets and hay should be available *ad libitum* and over a year only hay, which provides fibre, should be *ad lib*. Pellets or chows can be offered at approximately 1/4 cup per 5lbs of body weight per day. Overfeeding pellets to adult rabbits is a common cause of disease. To avoid this problem it is suggested that the rabbit is fed only when it has completely finished its last feed; it cannot then choose only the items it likes and leave the more nutritious portions. While they can eat any type of hay, alfalfa is too rich to be their sole hay. Fruits and vegetables should constitute 20% of the diet, with vegetables making up most of this 20%. Fresh produce is best and make sure it is thoroughly washed prior to feeding. As with many pets, variety is the key, so offer small amounts of several items. Avoid lettuce and celery as they are of little nutritional value but otherwise anything green and leafy is loaded with vitamins and is a good supplement.

Fresh water should be available 24 hours a day. If water is offered in a bowl the container should not be able to spill in the cage. Chew toys, suitable for dogs, such as commercially available dog-chew or well-boiled meat bones, can be given and some owners offer wood to chew, which helps control growth of the incisors.

Rabbits should not require extra vitamins if their food is optimum. To help control hairballs, veterinary surgeons may prescribe a cat laxative which can be given daily or every few days. Others find that pineapple juice is a useful measure to control hair balls in long haired rabbits.

Coprophagy

Rabbits engage in coprophagy, which means they eat their own faeces. This occurs at night and these faecal pellets are different from the ones normally excreted and seen by the owners. These pellets serve as a vital source of nutrients, especially vitamins and allow the rabbit to make best use of his/her fibrous diet. Most owners never observe this behaviour but if you do, remember it is normal and necessary for the health of the rabbit. Also note that a rabbit which cannot easily bend round (for instance because of a back injury) will have difficulty with coprophagy and consequent gastrointestinal compromise.

HOUSING

Many rabbits are housed outside in a hutch, with access to a grass run. Some people like to keep rabbits inside and they can make good household pets. They should never be allowed to run loose in the house as they love to chew and can be very destructive to furniture and even electrical cord. A rabbit can be let out of its cage when you are in the room and you can supervise and play with him/her.

Most owners use a portable dog or cat carrier as a cage to transport their rabbit and use a towel as bedding. Wire rabbit cages are also suitable but to decrease foot trauma (which results in the condition sore hocks), at least half the wire floor should be covered with towelling, plastic glass, or wood. A concealed hiding area in the cage allows the rabbit to feel secure. Make sure the rabbit does not chew its towel bedding as it could be swallowed and contribute to an intestinal blockage.

The cage should also contain a litterbox - rabbits, like cats, easily learn to use one - and ceramic or steel food and water bowls (bowls are preferred for water, over droppers, which must be inspected daily for clogging of the nipple).

As rabbits are very sensitive to heat stroke it is critical to keep their environment at or below 26°C (80°F) and their hutch well ventilated.

Fig. 11

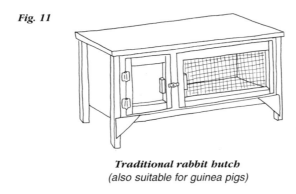

Traditional rabbit hutch
(also suitable for guinea pigs)

BREEDING

Like dogs and cats, female rabbits should be spayed early in life (by four-six months old). Whereas unspayed dogs and cats often develop malignant breast cancer and unspayed female ferrets die of anaemia, unspayed rabbits quite often develop malignant cancer of the uterus (uterine adenocarcinoma). This is relatively common in older rabbits and should be suspected whenever an unspayed female becomes sick. Diagnosis is difficult and often possible only during exploratory surgery.

The cost of the procedure is higher when the rabbit is sick (rabbits with uterine cancer normally need hospitalisation, fluid therapy and force feeding), so early spaying to prevent the problem is recommended.

Fig. 12

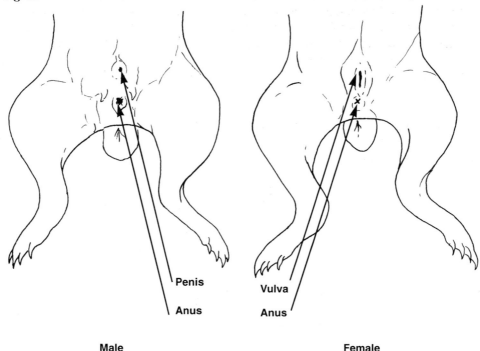

Penis

Anus

Vulva

Anus

Male　　　　　　　　　　　　　**Female**

External genitalia of adult rabbits

Note: ano-genital distance in the male.

COMMON PROBLEMS

These may be specific for a certain disease but most commonly they are vague and non-specific. A rabbit with anorexia (lack of appetite) and lethargy may have hairballs, uterine cancer, even kidney or liver failure. Any deviation from normal should be a cause for concern and requires immediate evaluation by a veterinary surgeon.

Like dogs and cats, rabbits can contract various intestinal parasites, as well as external ones such as fleas, mange and ear mites. Any internal parasites should be detected at the yearly faecal exam and are easily treated. Which medication the veterinary surgeon prescribes depends upon the examination findings.

Antibiotic toxicity

Antibiotics given by mouth often cause gut problems in rabbits. Some reports warn against using any oral antibiotics in rabbits, whereas others mention specific problems with oral drugs such as penicillin or lincomycin. Antibiotic toxicity is one reason to make sure only medications recommended by a veterinary surgeon are used. If a rabbit develops diarrhoea while on any medication it should be stopped and veterinary help sought at once!

Cystic calculi (bladder stones)

Rabbits, like many other species, can develop bladder stones. Signs include urinating frequently, straining to urinate and blood in the urine. Often the stones can be palpated (felt) by a veterinary surgeon on examination of the abdomen and radiographs (X-rays) can confirm the diagnosis. Surgical removal of the stones cures the problem. Rabbits that have been eating a diet high in pellets (which may contribute to stone formation) can be weaned onto a diet lower in pellets and higher in hay which may prevent stone recurrence.

Dental disease

The classic picture of a rabbit for most people is the goofy buck-toothed Bugs Bunny of Disney fame or Dylan from the Magic Roundabout. While these seem healthy cartoon characters, rabbits with teeth which do not meet or which have poor enamel, are in a dangerous state. The rabbit's teeth grow throughout life and so incisor (front) teeth that do not wear each other down will grow until the upper ones bury themselves in the lower jaw gums and the lower ones poke way out of the mouth. A rabbit like this cannot eat or groom. If the molars or cheek teeth do not meet properly they wear unevenly, causing sharp spikes to form. These erode at the gums causing painful ulcers, again stopping the animal from feeding or grooming. The importance of continual food intake in rabbits is central to health, while grooming is essential to prevent problems like fly strike. Thus well-functioning teeth are absolutely essential to a rabbit's well-being.

Fig. 13

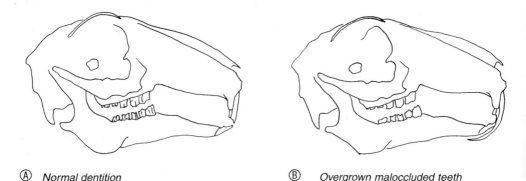

Ⓐ *Normal dentition*   Ⓑ *Overgrown maloccluded teeth*

Rabbit Skulls

One of the main reasons that teeth grow abnormally is that the bones of the jaw do not form properly due to deficiencies in calcium and other minerals. By giving a rabbit a big bowl of different foodstuffs, he can chose to eat only what he finds tasty. It is the less appetising items which often contain the minerals he needs. So give a small amount of rabbit mix or pellets as well as some greens and plenty of good-quality (ideally Timothy) hay so that he has eaten all the dry food by the time he has his next feed.

Assessment of the quality of a rabbit's teeth can be made by looking at the enamel surface. This should be smooth and shiny and not chipped or with an irregular surface.

Overgrown incisors should be shortened but this needs to be done regularly since the teeth keep growing. Vets used to clip rabbits' teeth with nail clippers but occasionally this damaged the teeth or gums. These days most vets seeing a large number of rabbits use dental burrs to file down the incisors. Treating poorly-aligned molar teeth is more difficult but filing rather than clipping is considered optimal today. One answer is to remove upper and lower incisors, a relatively simple operation. Although this sounds drastic it is without doubt the best long-term solution to the problem.

Diarrhoea/mucoid enteropathy

Diarrhoea is common in rabbits. While it can be due to coccidia (a one-cell protozoan) or incorrect use of oral antibiotics, often the cause cannot be determined. Rabbits eating a diet that is too high in carbohydrates (pellets or alfalfa hay) are more prone to develop intestinal problems than those eating a high fibre (grass hay) diet.

Mucoid enteropathy is a diarrhoeal disease of young rabbits that can be fatal. The diarrhoea has a mucoid or gelatinous consistency. Treatment for diarrhoeal conditions of rabbits is controversial and varies among vets. As a rule, fibre in the diet is increased (often nothing but hay is offered for several weeks). Fluid and vitamin therapy are used as needed.

Fly strike

During the summer months pet rabbits may be affected by maggot infestation. Different terms are used for this but fly strike is a common one. Another is to say that the rabbit is fly blown. The technical term a vet might use is myiasis. Healthy rabbits are generally not affected by fly strike. There are three main problems that lead to the condition. First, a wound to which the flies are attracted and on which they lay their eggs is an obvious site where maggots can cause damage. More commonly, a rabbit that cannot, or does not, turn round to groom will quickly have matted and soiled fur around its anus. This, from the fly's point of view, is an ideal opportunity to lay eggs. If the rabbit does not groom itself these fly larvae will hatch, survive and spread and may cause a tremendous amount of damage as they eat through the tissues. Thirdly, damp bedding is an ideal environment for egg-laying, maggot growth and development.

The key factors in preventing fly strike are to ensure that bedding is dry, that the rabbit does not have any wounds or ulcerated areas of skin and that there are no problems to prevent him grooming. These include dental disease and back immobility.

An animal which has sharp hooks on its molar or cheek teeth will not want to groom since these hooks cause pain when the rabbit extends its tongue to groom in the normal manner. Similarly, overgrown incisor teeth (at the front of the mouth) will impede grooming.

Rabbits with back problems may not be able to turn round to groom properly. Any rabbit with diarrhoea will be especially prone to fly strike and will have many other problems associated with the diarrhoea. Such a condition is an emergency for the rabbit far more than for a dog or cat (unless a puppy or kitten when, again, it is a major problem).

To treat fly strike the animal will need to be sedated or anaesthetised so that all the maggots can be removed and the whole area well disinfected with an antiseptic solution. The rabbit will need antibiotics since there is a major probability of secondary bacterial involvement. If the condition is severe intravenous fluids and steroids may be needed. In such a case the rabbit will be hospitalised and kept warm and comfortable, probably with a heat pad or an overhead infrared light. Such intensive care may cure the rabbit of the maggot infestation but in severe cases extensive surgery may be needed to remove all the dead maggot-ridden tissue. This can be a long, risky and often expensive treatment and it will still be necessary to overcome the original problems which led to the fly strike.

Owners should try to prevent fly strike by taking the rabbit to the veterinary surgeon maybe twice yearly for a routine health check (to ensure that dental disease or back problems are not imminent) and by providing dry, well-aired housing.

Hairballs

Hairballs (trichobezoars) are relatively common in rabbits. Like cats and ferrets, rabbits are very clean animals and love to groom themselves. Occasionally, a lot of hair can be swallowed during grooming and forms a ball in the stomach. Rabbits cannot vomit and, if the hair does not pass through the intestines they develop an obstruction. Hairballs are so common that they should always be suspected in a lethargic rabbit which is not eating. Diagnosis can be made on radiographs (X-rays) of the stomach: if the owner is sure the rabbit has not eaten within 24 hours and the radiographs show matter in the stomach, it is often a hairball. Sometimes, the diagnosis is made only during exploratory surgery.

Surgery should be a last resort, however, as the mortality rate from hairball surgery can be very high (about 50%). For very early mild cases, injections of drugs that alter intestinal motility may allow the obstruction to pass. The veterinary surgeon may also use fluid therapy and force feeding to help encourage the hairball to pass through the intestinal tract. Otherwise, surgery is needed and the earlier the surgery the better.

Many vets feel that regular cat hairball medicine helps prevent the problem. Feeding rabbits a diet high in hay (fibre) also helps prevent hairballs and other intestinal problems, as does daily brushing to remove excess dead hair. An interesting new development is feeding pineapple juice which, in early cases, may resolve the blockage without surgery.

Nail overgrowth

Rabbits have sharp nails and owners are easily scratched when handling their pets. The back feet, which are the most powerful, are usually the culprits. Scratches to owners most commonly occur when placing the rabbit back into its cage or down onto the floor. Supporting the rear end of the rabbit during the entire lifting, carrying, and replacing regimen will usually eliminate the problem (see above). Periodic nail trimming is important. Ask a vet to show you the proper technique.

Snuffles

This is the lay term given to respiratory infection mainly with the Pasteurella bacterium. Most commonly, clinical signs are related to the eyes (discharge, redness, squinting) or nose (sneezing, discharge). Often the eyes and nose are affected at the same time and Pasteurella can infect other areas of the body. Ear infections (resulting in a head tilt), abscesses (seen as lumps on the body) and uterine infections (often diagnosed only during exploratory surgery) also occur. Sudden death from septicaemia (infection in the blood) is rare but can occur.

Most cases of snuffles are mild. Treatment involves antibiotics but due to potential problems with many oral antibiotics, injections are often preferred. Eye drops and nose drops, prescribed by a veterinary surgeon, may be needed in selected cases.

Snuffles caused by Pasteurella is relatively easy to treat but hard, if not impossible, to cure. Like the kennel cough bacterium in dogs, most rabbits have Pasteurella, but only some show signs. Many rabbits are chronically infected, just as some children always seem to have a cold. The disease is easily transmitted

Fig. 14

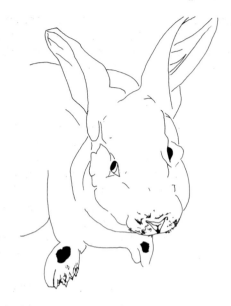

Rabbit with snuffles.

*Note mucopurulent discharge at the nose and also on the front
paws after nose rubbing, even in mild cases.*

by close contact between rabbits; new rabbits should be isolated (for about one month) before introducing them to existing pets. Stress situations, such as caused by a new cage mate, different diet or overcrowding, can cause relapse. Litter should be changed regularly to prevent ammonia accumulation from the urine which can irritate the eyes and nasal tissue.

Sore hocks

Sore hocks are common in rabbits. The hocks are essentially the ankles of rabbits and when a rabbit is sitting, which it does most of the time, its hocks are in contact with the cage floor. Often, wire-floored cages put too much pressure on the hocks, causing them to lose hair, turn red and become ulcerated and painful. The condition is usually prevented by supplying another surface to sit on such as a piece of wood, plastic glass, or a towel covering at least half the wire cage.

Treating sore hocks can be difficult and challenging, especially in the condition's later stages and requires antibacterial medications to clean the infected areas. Soft bedding is essential to allow the sores to heal. When caught early, the hocks can usually be treated without much effort. However, this can easily become a chronic, difficult-to-treat condition.

INFECTIOUS DISEASES

Two serious diseases caused by viruses are very common in the rabbit. They are myxomatosis and viral haemorrhagic disease. Every pet rabbit should be vaccinated against them and because they are viral diseases there are no effective treatments once the rabbit is infected.

Myxomatosis

This is caused by the myxoma virus which is widely distributed in the wild rabbit population. Owners might argue that their rabbit never comes into direct contact with animals from the wild and so does not need vaccination. The problem is that the virus is carried by rabbit fleas and mosquitoes so the disease can be passed on without direct contact. The incubation period is two days to a week and the first sign is the development of puffy eyelids and a purulent (pus-producing) conjunctivitis. Swelling under the skin extends around the eyes, ears and genital region. Death is usual 18 days to three weeks after infection but occasionally animals will survive and signs regress over three months.

Pregnant animals should not be vaccinated nor rabbits under six weeks old. Occasionally there is a local reaction at the injection site but compared with the lethal infection of many unvaccinated animals this is insignificant.

Viral haemorrhagic disease (VHD)

This was first noticed in China many years ago but now has an almost world-wide distribution and is seen more and more in the UK. Viral haemorrhagic disease is caused by a calicivirus, and although the incubation period is up to three days, animals may die suddenly without any clinical signs. If there are signs they include anorexia (not eating), pyrexia (fever), apathy and prostration. There may be convulsions and coma, dyspnoea (difficulty breathing), a mucoid foaming at the mouth or a bloody nasal discharge. Some animals survive this acute phase but die a few weeks later of liver disease and jaundice.

Given the horrendous death experienced by affected rabbits, every rabbit should be vaccinated annually or even every six months in areas where the disease is rampant.

Two other infectious diseases of rabbits are *Encephalitozoon cuniculi* and *Pasteurella multocida*.

Encephalitozoon cuniculi

Encephalitozoon cuniculi, also known as *Nosema cuniculi*, causes a chronic latent condition in rabbits with active disease characterised by neurological signs such as seizures, paralysis and eventually coma. There are no particularly effective drugs to treat the disease although sulphonamide antibiotics may be useful. Encephalitozoonosis has been described in a few cases in people but its significance is not really known. This underlines the importance of always washing hands after handling any animal and particularly before eating or preparing food.

Pasteurella multocida

Pasteurella is a bacterium which commonly causes abscesses and inflammatory disease in rabbits. It has already been discussed above in the context of snuffles but can infect the nasolacrimal (tear) duct and can cause abscesses in tooth roots, skin, the middle ear or internal organs. Note that many rabbits have Pasteurella but show no signs of disease. Only when the rabbit is under stress can the bacterium start to cause overt clinical problems. Treatment may include antibiotics but these do not penetrate well into the pus produced by Pasteurella infection. Surgery is possible if the abscess is in or under the skin but abscesses in the middle ear (causing balance problems), in the eyeball (causing blindness) or in the internal organs, are less easy to treat. As some form of stress probably triggers clinical disease, it is important to keep your rabbit as healthy as possible.

RATS

Rats are kept for many reasons, from being children's friends to prize show animals. They are excellent intelligent pets, are easy to keep and one can develop good owner-pet relationships with them.

Many rats sold as pets are white, although many other colours are available. 'Selfs' have one body colour which may be black, blue, chocolate, fawn etc. 'Hooded' animals have coloured heads and white bodies. Specific varieties include the Irish black (a white triangle of fur on the chest and white feet) and the Japanese hooded rat (stripe along the back with a solid-coloured head and shoulders with white body). If an owner wants to breed and show rats The National Fancy Rat Society (see useful addresses) will provide all the information needed.

Table 9

Normal biological information

Adult weight	400 - 800 g
Litter size	6 - 16 (average ten)
Gestation	20 - 22 days
Oestrous cycle	4 - 5 days
Duration of oestrus	14 hours
Weaning age	3 - 4 weeks
Life-span	3 - 4 years
Sexual maturity	6 - 10 weeks
Rectal temperature	38°C
Heart rate	260 - 450 per minute
Respiratory rate	70 - 150 per minute

HANDLING

Rats are generally amenable to handling and, although they rarely bite, they should always be handled with care. Grasping the rat firmly by the shoulders is the best way and a confidently held rat will be a much happier animal than one held gingerly. Handling a rat by the scruff is likely to cause distress and should be avoided.

FEEDING

Rats can be fed a commercial complete ration supplemented with fruit and vegetables. They are happy to eat tit bits and chocolate but, while these can be useful in firming the owner-pet bond, they can lead to obesity and considerable health problems.

HOUSING

Rats can be housed successfully in commercial or home-built cages. If advising on making a cage remember that rats can chew through wood or plastic very easily and, once free, will gnaw everything from household items to electrical cables. Metal and glass are good materials for cages, which often include a separate bedding area; although this is unnecessary if there is sufficient space. Most cages are too small. A floor space 60 x 50 cm (24 x 20 in) with a height of 40 cm (16 in) will cater for two or three rats but basically the bigger the better. Any wire mesh should be fine enough to prevent escape of young rats but sturdy enough to resist the teeth of adults.

Bedding, either tissue paper or soft wood shavings, which will need regular cleaning. This is a very good reason for a hard plastic base to the cage, which should be sterilised regularly. Rats should be housed at between 14-26°C (58-80°F) and never above 30°C (88°F) since fatal heat stroke is then possible.

BREEDING

Adult rats can be sexed easily but young animals are more difficult. The anus and vulva in the female are much closer together than the anus and penis in the male. Rats are sexually mature at six to ten weeks and have a gestation of 20 to 22 days with a litter size of six to 16, average ten. Weaning age is three to four weeks. Population explosions are common when rats are kept in groups. Ideally they should be housed in either single-sex groups or in single-sex pairs. It is recommended that a male - female pair be separated before the birth of young because within 12 hours they will mate, causing a very rapid increase in the pet population!

COMMON PROBLEMS

A rat's lifespan is only three to four years so ageing changes and natural fatal conditions such as tumours are fairly common. Here we cover the more common conditions that owners should recognise so that they know when to take their rat to a veterinary surgeon. Many people think it is not worth taking a pet rat to the vet but those with rats as pets or show animals can become very attached to them.

Antibiotic toxicities

All pet rodents are sensitive to certain antibiotics. Several of these antibiotics can be fatal; this is true whether the antibiotics are given orally, by injection or topically (via the skin) but is particularly the case in antibiotics given by mouth which upset the normal bacteria found in the gut of the rodent. Examples of toxic antibiotics include penicillin and related drugs, bacitracin, erythromycin, lincomycin, tylosin and streptomycin. Owners should never use antibiotics in or on their pet rodents without first consulting a veterinary surgeon experienced in rodent medicine.

Diarrhoea

This is common in rats and can be caused by a wide range of infectious organisms. These range from bacteria, through single-celled organisms like coccidia to parasites such as tapeworms. Among the bacteria are two of particular importance: Salmonella and *Bacillus piliformis*. Salmonella can pass from animals to man therefore any diarrhoeic faeces should be cultured to ensure Salmonella is not the cause. An animal with Salmonella may have to be put down but other bacteria can sometimes be treated with a drop of antibiotic (such as neomycin) by mouth. *Bacillus piliformis* causes Tyzzer's disease which often results in generalised illness and death. Antibiotic treatment may be effective but prevention is preferable and a quarantine period for new animals coming into a collection is important.

Mammary tumours

Cancer of the mammary glands is very common in rats. It is sometimes malignant and in such cases the prognosis is very poor. Nevertheless rats are less affected by malignant mammary tumours than are mice and many masses will be benign and can be removed surgically. Even if malignant, the prolongation of life by a couple of months is significant in animals with such a short lifespan.

Pneumonia

Pneumonia is a common problem in rats and occurs often in larger colonies rather than animals kept individually or in small groups. Animals with breathing difficulties, a hunched posture and loss of general condition may have respiratory problems caused by viruses, the organism mycoplasma or bacteria.

Ringworm

The skin fungus ringworm is common in rats. A veterinary surgeon will diagnose ringworm either by using an ultraviolet light, under which the ringworm lesions on the skin fluoresce, or by taking a small amount of hair and examining it under the microscope. This will also show if there are any fur mites causing the skin problem. Ringworm can be treated with medication (griseofulvin) by mouth; mites can be treated with an injection of the drug ivermectin.

Sialodacryoadenitis (red tears)

Red tears, often seen in rats and mice, can result from viral or bacterial disease or stress. Often it is hard to tell what is actually causing the problem which looks as if blood is coming from the eyes. In viral infection, usually the salivary and Harderian glands (those at the inner corner of the eye) are involved. Because rodents have porphyrins (pigments) in their tears, any discharge will be seen as red. Treatment is symptomatic and involves topical eye medication.

Weil's disease

This is a disease caused by leptospira, which can affect humans but is not found in pet animals in captivity. Owners worried that their animal maybe harbouring the disease can be reassured that it is a problem only in wild rats.

This is only a small survey of the problems you may see in pet rats. Many diseases are related to poor husbandry, showing the importance in advising keeping the pet in the best possible conditions.

REPTILES

REPTILES

SELECTION

Reptiles are popular pets, although many are really not suitable to be kept without a significant amount of work and understanding of their needs. Some people want to own them to be different (never a good reason for owning any pet), some enjoy the lower cost of veterinary care as compared with dogs and cats (this is often, but not always true) and many people who do not have the time to devote to a dog or cat enjoy the relatively 'maintenance-free' appeal of a snake, iguana or tortoise. Before buying a reptile, it would be wise to suggest that potential owners ask themselves several questions:

Do I want a pet to handle and socialise?

While many reptiles, especially those purchased as captive-born infants, allow owners to handle them, others do not. Many of the more exotic species such as chameleons do not allow handling and react aggressively or become severely stressed. As a rule, if you want a pet to snuggle with, a reptile is not for you. If, on the other hand, you want an animal you can display, a reptile deserves your consideration.

How much time can I devote to my pet?

All pets require at least 15 minutes of observation by the owner each day. The owner who fails to pay at least this much attention to his pet will not detect early signs of disease and is really neglecting his or her responsibility as an owner. Most reptiles need to be fed and watered daily and often the cage needs to be cleaned daily. The person who intends to put his reptile in a cage and observe it only occasionally should not own this type of pet.

Can I afford proper medical care?

All reptiles need to be examined within 48 hours of purchase by a veterinary surgeon, ideally one with a specific interest in reptiles (see The first veterinary visit, below). Yearly health checks are advised but there are no vaccinations required for a reptile. Apart from this any illness requires full veterinary attention which can be just as expensive as with a dog or cat.

Can I make the correct habitat (home) for my reptile?

At a minimum, most reptiles require a ten-gallon glass aquarium, some 'cage furniture', a source of heat and a source of UV light. While not expensive or difficult to assemble, an improper environment is the second most common source of diseases and captivity problems in reptiles with generally, the most common problem being an incorrect diet.

Fig. 15

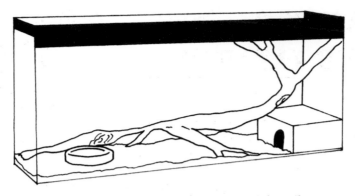

An appropriate vivarium for a terrestrial reptile
Note: water bowl, branch for climbing and rubbing against when shedding, and hideaway box.

Reptiles do become sick and preventing illness is definitely preferred to treatment. As an introduction to reptile diseases, owners should understand that reptiles hide signs of illness. This is called the 'preservation response'. In the wild, if an animal showed signs of illness every time it felt off-colour, it could be attacked by predators or even members of its own group. Therefore, these animals do not appear ill until the problem is advanced. Our pet reptiles still retain this 'wild' characteristic. A sick reptile is a dying reptile. It is very important owners take their pet to the veterinary surgeon at the first sign of illness. Waiting to see if things get better or treating with over-the-counter medications, especially those sold at pet shops, only delays proper treatment and often results in expensive veterinary bills and a dead reptile! Veterinary surgeons can do many things for sick reptiles but early intervention is critical.

While the principles of diagnosis and treatment of diseases are the same regardless of the species of pet, there are important differences between reptiles and dogs and cats. Ideally if keeping a reptile it is important to build a relationship with a veterinary surgeon with expertise in treating reptiles before the reptile shows any signs of ill health.

THE FIRST VETERINARY VISIT

This includes determining the animal's weight and checking for lumps and bumps. The pet should be examined for signs of dehydration or starvation and a faecal test to check for internal parasites. It is impossible to get a reptile to defecate on command (although many will give you an unwelcome sample if angered!). The oral cavity should be examined for signs of infectious stomatitis (mouth rot). No vaccines are required for reptiles. Most of the visit will probably be a question-and-answer session about how the reptile is being kept and what its normal behaviour is like. If all turns out well the pet will be given a clean bill of health. Just like dogs and cats, reptiles should be examined and have their stool tested for parasites annually.

IGUANAS & OTHER LIZARDS

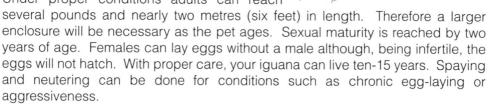

IGUANAS

The green iguana is a popular lizard pet. Under proper conditions adults can reach several pounds and nearly two metres (six feet) in length. Therefore a larger enclosure will be necessary as the pet ages. Sexual maturity is reached by two years of age. Females can lay eggs without a male although, being infertile, the eggs will not hatch. With proper care, your iguana can live ten-15 years. Spaying and neutering can be done for conditions such as chronic egg-laying or aggressiveness.

ANATOMY

Mature males (two years and older) are easily distinguished from females as they have larger and more pronounced femoral pores on the inner aspects of the thighs. These pores are openings of glands used in marking behaviours.

Fig. 16

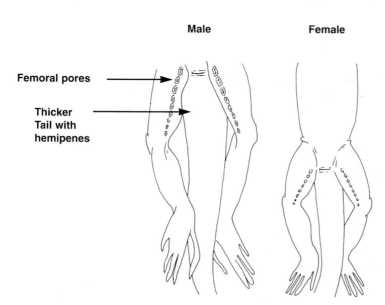

Male   **Female**

Femoral pores ——————→

Thicker
Tail with
hemipenes ——————→

External appearance of adult iguanas

Iguanas have a renal portal blood system, where blood from the hind limbs is filtered by the kidneys before reaching the general circulation. This means toxins from the rear legs (as could occur from wounds) or drugs injected into the hind legs may seriously affect the kidneys in reptiles. They excrete uric acid as their main waste product of protein metabolism (dogs, cats and humans excrete urea). This allows them to adapt to desert environments where water supply might be restricted.

Iguanas and other lizards have a cloaca which receives secretions from the urinary, gastrointestinal and reproductive systems and males have two reproductive organs called hemipenes. The skin is covered with scales and is usually shed in patches, unlike a snake's skin which is generally shed in one piece.

Table 10

Biological data for selected species

	Common iguana (*iguana iguana*)	Leopard gecko (*Eublepharus macularius*)	Green anole (*Anolis carolinesis*)
Region	Central & South America	Western Asia	North America
Environment			
Habitat	Arboreal	Terrestrial	Arboreal
Diet	Herbivorous	Insectiverous	Insectiverous* carnivorous
Temp. °C	26 - 30	23 - 30	23 - 30
Humidity %	60 - 80	60 - 80	70 - 80
Reproduction	Oviparous	Oviparous	Oviparous
Sexual maturity	70 cm (2 - 3 yrs)	2 - 4 years	6 months
Gestation (days)	63 - 73	47 - 100 (depends on temp. @ 27°C - 60 days)	60-90
Incubation Temp. °C	30	26 - 35	28-30
Relative humidity %	75	80 - 100	80 - 100
Clutch size (eggs)	25 - 40	Up to 6 cutches/yr	Small clutches (diff. to hatch)
Size (adult)	100 - 150 cm	25 cm	10 - 15 cm

*   *Principal dietary requirement*

SELECTION

Most owners buy iguanas locally from a pet shop, although ordering from reptile breeders may be possible. Young, captive-raised animals make the best pets. Older imports are harder to tame, may harbour internal parasites and often suffer from the stress of captivity. Avoid sick-looking animals as many are terminally ill. Trying to nurse an iguana back to health after purchase rarely works - just the stress of a new environment is often enough to kill it.

Avoid lizards that appear thin, have loose skin or sunken eyes and appear inactive or lethargic. A healthy iguana is usually bright green, active and alert. The vent or cloaca should be clean and free of wetness or stool. If you can gently open the mouth (tapping lightly on the snout with a finger often works), there should be a small amount of clear saliva present and a bright pink tongue and oral cavity. Mucus that is cloudy or like cottage cheese is a sign of mouth rot, as are redness or pinpoint haemorrhages on the mucous membranes. Always inquire about a guarantee in case the iguana is found to be unhealthy.

Within 48 hours the new iguana should be examined by a veterinary surgeon, ideally one with experience in reptiles. The vet will determine its weight and check for lumps and bumps and signs of dehydration/starvation. A faecal sample should be tested for internal parasites. The vet will check the iguana's mouth for infectious stomatitis (mouth rot) and may recommend blood tests, cultures or radiographs (X-rays) to check for other diseases. Iguanas do not need any vaccinations but, like all pets, they should have an annual examination including a faecal test for parasites.

FEEDING

The iguana is mainly herbivorous (eats plants) and the reptile's hind-gut is highly specialised to allow fibre digestion, similar to the stomach compartments of a cow.

While some veterinary surgeons recommend only plant material for iguanas, many others feel that supplementing a plant-based diet with about five to 20% animal-based protein such as crickets, meal worms, moths or reptile pellets is acceptable. A guide that has worked well for many iguanas is: juveniles (less than two) - 80% plant-based protein, 20% animal-based protein; adults (over two) - 90-100% plant-based protein, 0-10% animal-based protein. Discuss this with your vet. Most young iguanas eat daily; older ones can be fed daily or every other day, depending on appetite.

Most (80-90%) of the plant material should be flowers and vegetables with around 10-20% fruits. As a rule, anything green and leafy should make up a large part of the diet plus yellow and orange vegetables. Avoid fibre-rich, vitamin-deficient vegetables including lettuce and celery; their composition is mainly fibre and water with few vitamins or minerals. Acceptable vegetables include a mixture of greens, such as mustard, turnip or carrot greens, alfalfa hay, kale, parsley, spinach (in small amounts), green beans, peas, corn, tofu (soya beans), cabbage or broccoli (also in small amounts) and flowers such as carnations, hibiscus and roses (avoid azaleas as they are toxic). Vegetables can be offered cooked or raw (thoroughly wash raw vegetables) to see which the iguana prefers. Flowers can be home-grown or bought and could be the older flowers which shops throw out. It is wise to ensure that no chemicals have been applied to the flowers or water. Fruit can include apples, pears, bananas, grapes, peaches, kiwis and melons. Fruits that are particularly healthy include figs (which contain calcium), papaya, raspberries and strawberries.

If the veterinary surgeon decides that animal-based protein is acceptable, appropriate foods include crickets, sardines (drained), hard-boiled eggs, waxmoth larvae and meal worms. Dog food and cat food contain too much vitamin D and fat and should generally not be fed. Reptile pellets, bird pellets, trout chow and other fish meals are excellent protein sources.

Live prey, such as crickets and worms, should either be raised by the owner, retrieved from a nearby field, or purchased from a pet shop or reptile breeder. Care must be exercised when collecting insects, especially from the home garden as fertilisers and insecticides can be toxic to iguanas.

Vitamins

Many vets recommend lightly sprinkling all the food offered to the iguana with a calcium powder (calcium gluconate, lactate or carbonate). Weekly, a light sprinkling of a good reptile vitamin powder (such as SA-37 or Nutrobal) on the food is also recommended. A common problem in pet iguanas is over-supplementation with vitamins and minerals. Check with a veterinary surgeon about the need to supplement the diet.

Fresh water in a ceramic dish that will not easily tip over should be available at all times. Iguanas will not only drink from the water bowl but will often bathe in it (although it is perfectly acceptable to mist the iguana with water a few times a week too). Make sure the water stays clean; many iguanas love to defecate in their water bowl!

HOUSING

Small juvenile pets often do well in a ten- or 20-gallon aquarium. As the iguana grows, he must be moved to a more comfortable enclosure. Veterinary practices or pet shops may have examples of these to give an idea of the proper habitat for an adult iguana.

Substrate, or bedding material, should be easy to clean and nontoxic to the iguana. Newspaper, butcher's paper, towels or artificial turf is recommended. When using turf, buy two pieces and cut them to fit the bottom of the cage. Place one in the cage and keep the spare clean. When the turf in the cage becomes soiled replace it with the dry piece and clean the soiled turf with ordinary soap and water (avoid harsher products unless a vet says they are acceptable).

Alfalfa pellets can also be used for bedding and are often eaten by the iguana, which is acceptable. Avoid sand, gravel, wood shavings and cat litter, as these are not only difficult to clean but can cause impactions if eaten on purpose or accidentally, for example if food becomes contaminated. Note that cedar wood shavings are toxic to reptiles!

Iguanas enjoy natural branches in the enclosure but make sure they cannot fall and cause injury. Ideally, the branch should slope from the bottom of the enclosure to the top and end near a heat source so the iguana can bask. Rocks (large ones) also encourage basking. A hiding place is appreciated by all reptiles and can be created using artificial plants, clay pots, cardboard boxes or other containers.

A heat source is necessary for all reptiles as they are cold-blooded and need a range of temperatures to regulate their internal body temperature. Ideally, the cage should be set up so that one end is warmer than the other. In this way, the iguana can move around its environment and warm or cool itself as needed. Put a thermometer at the cooler end of the cage and another at the end near the heat source. The cooler end should be 21-24°C (70-75°F); the warmer end 32-38°C (90-100°F). An inexpensive way to do this is to use a 100-watt incandescent bulb with a reflector hood, although pet shops sell other types of heat lamps. The heat source should be placed outside and above one end of the cage, which should be covered by a screen to prevent the iguana from escaping or burning itself on the bulb. At night, heat is not necessary as long as the temperature remains at 19-22°C (65-70°F).

Heating pads can also be used. Discuss with a veterinary surgeon the correct way to use them if you choose this form of heating. Hot rocks or sizzle rocks are dangerous and ineffective and should be avoided!

Ultra violet light is also necessary (to provide vitamin D-3). Without UV light your iguana will be predisposed to metabolic bone disease, common in pet iguanas. The source should emit light in the UV-B range (290-320 nanometers). Combining a black light with a Vita-Lite, Chroma-50 or Colortone-50 in a two-bulb fixture is an excellent way to provide UV light, although many iguanas do well with just a Vita-Lite. The vet may recommend other brands. The UV output of these lights decreases with age; they should be replaced every six months. For UV light to work it must reach the pet in an unfiltered form, so make sure there is no glass or plastic between the light and your iguana. Finally, the light should be 15-30 cm (6-12 inches) from the pet to ensure any benefit.

COMMON PROBLEMS

Signs of disease in iguanas may be specific for a certain disease, such as jaw or hind limb swelling in metabolic bone disease, or non-specific, such as anorexia (lack of appetite) and lethargy, which can be seen with many diseases. Any deviation from normal should be a cause for concern and requires immediate evaluation by a veterinary surgeon.

Abscesses

These appear as hard tumour-like swellings anywhere on the pet's body. Abscesses are treated surgically: the cavity is opened and flushed with a medicated solution. A culture of the abscess may be needed to determine the type of infection and thus which antibiotic should be used. Topical medication and injectable antibiotics may also be used.

Avascular necrosis

Iguanas may be afflicted with this condition in which blood flow to the affected body part, usually the tip of the tail or one of the digits (toes), is blocked. Without a blood supply the body part starts to become necrotic or die. Within a short time the toe or tip of the tail becomes discoloured and possibly infected. The necrosis or infection can spread up the tail or to other toes. Several things can cause the blood vessels to become blocked, such as infection, a blood clot (embolus) in another part of the body shifting to the tail or toe, trauma causing damage to the blood vessels or a tumour cutting off blood supply to the part. Usually, the cause is not determined. Treatment involves amputating the affected part in an effort to stop the spread of the necrosis. Most pets recover well and lead normal lives after the surgery.

Cystic calculi (bladder stones)

These commonly occur when minerals from the diet form crystals in the urine which then form stones. Usually these are composed of uric acid which often results from a diet that contains too much protein (e.g. one high in dog or cat food).

Blood may be detected in the iguana's droppings if he/she has calculi. An examination and radiographs (X-rays) allow a veterinary surgeon to diagnose the problem. Surgical removal of the stones is needed, as is fluid therapy to prevent kidney damage. The vet will discuss dietary correction in an attempt to prevent further stones.

Hypervitaminosis D

Hypervitaminosis D develops if owners either over-supplement the iguana's diet with vitamins and minerals or feed dog or cat food. Clinical signs are vague and include lack of appetite and lethargy. It is a serious condition that requires hospitalisation and intensive therapy with fluids, force feeding and drugs such as diuretics and corticosteroids to help lower the iguana's calcium levels.

Infectious stomatitis

Infectious stomatitis (mouth rot) is seen as pinpoint haemorrhages on the gums or an excess of thick mucus, often like cottage cheese, in the mouth. It usually requires injectable antibiotics and antibiotic and antiseptic mouth rinses. Atropine (to dilute the oral secretions) and vitamin C may be needed.

Metabolic bone disease

Metabolic bone disease, probably the most common problem, is usually caused by feeding a diet low in calcium or vitamin D and high in phosphorus. Common signs include swelling of the lower jaw and/or the hind limbs. As the condition progresses muscle twitching, loss of appetite and loss of energy (lethargy) develop.

Calcium deficiency is manifest in bones which fracture easily and have swollen cortices (the structural cylinders of long bones). This usually requires injectable or oral calcium, a multivitamin or mineral supplement. The veterinary surgeon may recommend a form of calcitonin, a drug which mimics natural calcitonin, a hormone stimulating the iguana to deposit calcium into the bone.

Parasites

Parasites, especially pinworms, are common in pet iguanas. Often they do not cause clinical signs and are detected only on annual faecal exam, however they may cause diarrhoea or weight loss. Several deworming medications are available either as an oral or injectable drug. The type of parasite identified on the microscopic faecal examination will determine which drug is needed.

Salmonella

While terrapins are most commonly incriminated for causing Salmonella bacterial infections in people, iguanas have lately been determined to be a source of this infection. This bacterium can cause severe gastrointestinal disease or septicaemia (blood poisoning). Many animals and people carry the bacteria without showing any clinical signs yet shed the bacteria in their faeces which can infect others.

Prevention, through proper hygiene, is the best way to control the disease. Simple precautions such as always washing hands after touching the iguana or its bedding are ones which should be taken with any pets not just reptiles. Since most iguanas which carry Salmonella are not ill, they usually require no treatment (treatment often fails to kill the bacterium anyway).

OTHER LIZARDS

Many of the problems seen in other lizards are similar to those as described for iguanas. With regard to diet and husbandry, however, each individual species has its own requirement, depending on its diet and environment in the wild. While some are desert species others live in rain forest environments - clearly these species will have very different captive husbandry requirements (for further information see Mattison, 1997).

SNAKES

Several species of snakes are commonly kept as pets. These include king snakes, garter snakes, Burmese pythons, various boa constrictors and Royal or ball pythons. The needs of each species differ from those of the generic snake, so be sure to discuss these needs with a veterinary surgeon, ideally one experienced in treating snakes. The python will be used for this discussion as it is probably the most common species of pet snake. Most of the information concerning the Royal or ball python is applicable to other terrestrial snakes. As noted in the discussion of lizards, snakes from different habitats require different captive requirements.

Many snakes sold as pets are easy to handle and non-aggressive. Many, especially the Royal, or ball python, may not eat for weeks to months after the stress of going to a new environment. This can be normal, or can be a sign of a more serious disease that requires prompt veterinary attention. One major cause of anorexia is that the snake does not see dead white mice as food. Live prey should never be fed - apart from being cruel to the mouse to enclose it with its predator, the snake may be bitten and injured considerably by the mouse. A food item offered should be made to appear alive by moving it around. Also brown rodents are probably better accepted than are white mice.

Ideally, pets purchased should be captive-bred animals. Wild-caught snakes are less tolerant of stress, more likely to refuse to feed and often harbour internal and external parasites. In addition obtaining a wild animal further depletes wild populations, many of which are already in decline.

Male and female snakes look very similar; a veterinary surgeon will be able to demonstrate the difference (Fig. 16). Hatchling ball pythons are about 30 cm (12 inches) long and grow to about one metre (three feet) by three years of age. At maturity (in three-five years), adults reach 150-180 cm (five-six feet). Depending upon their care, ball pythons can live ten-20 years. Note this increase in size in the larger species of pythons and boas: a small youngster can turn into quite a handful!

ANATOMY

Most snakes have only one functional, simple lung (usually the right). This extends at least one third of the snake's body length. Snakes have a cloaca, a common opening for the urinary, digestive and genital tracts. Males have two reproductive organs called hemipenes. With some snakes it is possible to sex them by observing the tail morphology but probing with a specially designed blunt sexing probe is the best method: the male with its paired hemipenes has a longer blind ending sac caudal to the cloaca. Of course, snakes have no limbs but there are spurs in the cloacal region of some snakes which represent vestigial limbs. They have numerous pairs of ribs and have a three-chambered heart; people, dogs and cats have four-chambered hearts.

Snakes do not have diaphragms so cannot cough or clear their airways and those with simple respiratory infections easily develop pneumonia. Respiratory infections in reptiles are always more serious than similar infections in mammals. Snakes have fused eyelids which form a transparent spectacle.

Fig. 17

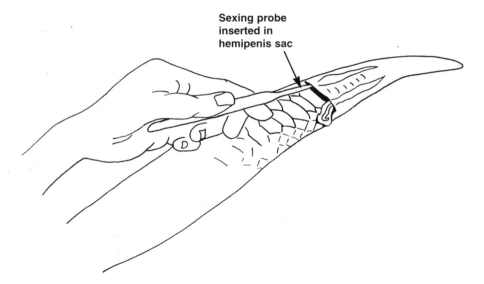

**Sexing probe
inserted in
hemipenis sac**

Sexing a male snake
(redrawn after Mader, 1996)

Table 11

Biological data for selected species

	Boa constrictor (*Boa constrictor constrictor*)	Indian Python (*Python molurus*)
Region	Central & South America	Asia
Environment		
Habitat	Arboreal	Arboreal
Diet	Carnivorous	Carnivorous
Temp. °C	25 - 30	25 - 30
Humidity %	50 - 70	70 - 80
Reproduction	Viviparous	Oviparous
Gestation	approx. 6 months	65 - 70 days
Incubation Temp. °C		30
Relative humidity %		80 - 100
Sexual maturity	1.5 m	2.5 m (*m*) 3.5 m (*f*) (18 - 24 months)
Litter size/clutch size (live young/eggs)	20 (up to 60 reported)	20 - 50
Size (adult)	400 cm - usually smaller	600 cm

SELECTION

Most owners buy snakes locally from a pet shop, although ordering from reptile breeders may be possible. A prospective owner should know what he is getting and should ask about a guarantee if the pet is found to be unhealthy. Young, captive-raised animals make the best pets. Older imported animals are harder to tame, may harbour internal parasites and often suffer from the stress of captivity. Snakes that appear skinny, have loose skin or sunken eyes and appear inactive should be avoided. A healthy snake is usually bright, active and alert. The eyes should be clear; cloudy eyes usually indicate the snake is about to shed. While not a sign of illness, shedding is very stressful to snakes and it would be best to purchase a snake that is not about to shed. When the eyes are examined they should be checked for mites, which are tiny black dots that often move. There should be no lumps or bumps; simply running the hands slowly down the snake's body should detect any swellings. The vent or cloaca should be clean and free of wetness or stool stuck to it. If possible, the mouth should be opened gently to reveal a small amount of clear saliva and a pink tongue. Mucus that is cloudy or cottage cheese-like is a sign of mouth rot, as is redness or pinpoint haemorrhaging on the mucous membranes.

FEEDING

Unlike most pets, snakes eat whole small mammals including mice, rats, gerbils and hamsters. Larger snakes will eat whole rabbits.

Since snakes eat entire prey items, this simplifies things for their owners and prevents many dietary diseases so common in other reptiles. However, there is the problem of providing prey. If potential purchasers are squeamish about killing rodents a snake is probably not for them!

Ideally, a snake should be provided either a thawed (previously frozen) prey item or a freshly-killed one. Feeding live prey is not recommended: the prey obviously knows it is prey and unless killed and eaten immediately, suffers psychological stress given that it will be in an environment where it cannot escape from its predator. Second (and surprising for most snake-owners) is the fact that even a small mouse can quite severely injure a snake if the snake isn't hungry! For humane reasons and for the snake's safety, strongly consider feeding dead prey.

How often a snake is fed depends upon his/her size and age. Smaller snakes usually eat twice each week and larger snakes eat once per week to once every few weeks. Ask a veterinary surgeon for guidance. A snake's response will also tell you how often he needs to eat. If he does not eat there are many possible causes, such as the stress of a new environment, shedding, pregnancy or breeding-season anorexia. Failure to eat could also be a sign of cancer, kidney failure, gout or parasites. A veterinary surgeon can help determine the cause of anorexia after a thorough physical examination and appropriate laboratory testing.

As a rule snakes do not need extra vitamins. However, since a snake 'is what he eats', it is important to make sure the prey is healthy and well fed. For this reason many owners raise their own rodents for feeding to their snakes. It would not hurt to insert a multi-vitamin/mineral tablet into the stomach or abdomen of the dead prey prior to feeding the snake, but first check this with a veterinary surgeon.

Fresh water (in a ceramic dish that won't easily tip over) should be available at all times. Snakes will not only drink from the water bowl but will often bathe in it (although it is perfectly acceptable to mist the snake with water a few times a week too). Make sure the water stays clean; many snakes love to defecate in their water bowl.

HOUSING

Smaller juvenile pets often do well in a ten- or 20-gallon aquarium, or even large plastic lunch boxes (with small air holes cut for ventilation). As the snake grows, he must be moved to a more comfortable enclosure. A veterinary practice or pet shop may have examples of these larger enclosures to indicate the proper habitat for an adult snake.

Substrate, or bedding material in the cage should be easy to clean and non toxic to the snake. Newspaper, butcher's paper, towels or artificial turf is recommended. When using turf, two pieces should be cut to fit the bottom of the cage. One should be placed in the cage and the other kept clean so that when the turf inside the cage becomes soiled, there will be a clean, dry piece to replace it. The soiled turf can be cleaned with ordinary soap and water (harsher products should be avoided unless a veterinary surgeon says they are acceptable), thoroughly rinsed and hung to dry, to be used at the next cage cleaning.

Sand, gravel, wood shavings, corn cob material, walnut shells and cat litter should be avoided, as these are not only difficult to clean but can cause impaction if eaten on purpose or accidentally should the food become covered by these substrates. Cedar wood shavings are toxic to reptiles so avoid using them.

Snakes enjoy natural branches but make sure they are secure and cannot fall onto the snake. Ideally, the branch should slope from the bottom of the enclosure to the top, ending near a heat source so the snake can bask. Rocks (large ones) in the cage also allow for basking. All reptiles appreciate a hiding place, which can be created using artificial plants, clay pots, cardboard boxes or other containers.

A heat source is necessary for all reptiles, which are cold-blooded and need a range of temperatures to regulate their internal body temperature. Ideally, the cage should be set up so that a heat gradient is established, with one end of the tank warmer than the other. In this way, the snake can move around its environment and warm or cool itself as needed. The owner should buy two thermometers and place one at the cooler end of the cage and one at the warmer end near the heat source. The cooler end of the cage should be 21-24°C (approximately 70-75°F), while the warmer end should be 32-35°C (90-95°F) but remember that the optimal temperature range will depend on what the animal is used to in its wild habitat. An inexpensive way to provide heat is to supply a focal heat source using a 100-watt incandescent bulb with a reflector hood, although pet shops sell other types of heat lamps. The heat source should be placed outside and above one end of the cage, which should be covered by a screen top to prevent the snake from escaping or burning itself on the bulb. At night, heat is not necessary as long as the temperature remains 19-21°C (65-70°F).

Heating pads can also be used; a snake owner should ask a veterinary surgeon to explain the correct way to use them. Hot rocks or sizzle rocks however are dangerous, ineffective and should be avoided!

While UV light is necessary to provide vitamin D-3 for most reptiles, veterinary surgeons are divided about the need for UV light for snakes. This is because snakes consume whole prey which should be nutritionally balanced. UV light would not be harmful and may be beneficial, so it may be wise to provide some type of UV light such as a Vita-Lite. Potential owners should discuss this with a veterinary surgeon.

COMMON PROBLEMS

Anorexia

Anorexia means lack of appetite or refusal to feed. Snakes commonly exhibit this. It can be a condition which occurs because of natural changes or an environment or diet which is slightly sub-optimal. It is often associated with pregnancy, the breeding season, incorrect environment, incorrect diet or, most commonly, the stress of a new environment. 'Abnormal' anorexia is most often caused by a disease such as infectious stomatitis (mouth rot), parasites, kidney failure or gout. A veterinary surgeon will need to perform a thorough physical examination and run laboratory tests to make sure the anorexia is not caused by a specific disease. Getting the snake who suffers from 'normal' anorexia to eat is a challenge but is usually successful with time and patience.

Infectious stomatitis

Infectious stomatitis (mouth rot) is seen as pinpoint haemorrhages on the gums or excess thick mucus, often like cottage cheese, in the mouth. In severe cases, the snake will have severe swelling of the mouth and exhibit open-mouth breathing.

The snake usually requires injectable antibiotics and antibiotic mouth rinses. Atropine (to reduce the thickness of the oral secretions) and vitamin C may also be needed.

Lumps and bumps

Snakes are commonly seen with various lumps and bumps on or within their bodies. Various conditions can cause these. External lumps can be caused by infections (as is the case with abscesses), tumours or parasites. Internal swelling can be caused by organ problems (such as kidney disease or parasitic infections of the stomach), retained eggs in some species of snakes, tumours and even constipation!

A veterinary surgeon may need to run tests to determine the cause of the swelling. Once this is known, the vet will decide if medical or surgical therapy is best. Many lumps and bumps are benign, not life-threatening; others are signs of serious disease. The sooner a snake is examined, the better its chances of recovery.

Parasites

Parasites are common in pet snakes. They often cause no clinical signs and are detected on an annual faecal examination. They may, however, cause diarrhoea or weight loss. Several deworming medications are available either as an oral or injectable drug. The type of parasite identified on the microscopic faecal examination will determine which drug is needed.

Respiratory infections

Most respiratory infections are caused by bacteria and, in snakes, are often seen with mouth rot. Snakes with respiratory infections may have excess mucus in their oral cavities, nasal discharge, lethargy and loss of appetite and possibly open-mouth breathing and wheezing. Respiratory infections are most often caused by bacteria; other organisms, including parasites, can cause respiratory problems as well. The examining veterinary surgeon may want to take radiographs (X-rays), blood tests and cultures to determine the cause of the infection. Treatment for infections involves antibiotics given orally or injected. Sick snakes require intensive care, including fluid therapy and force feeding, in the hospital.

Salmonella

While terrapins are most commonly incriminated in spreading Salmonella bacteria to their owners, any reptile, including snakes, can carry the bacterium. It can cause severe gastrointestinal disease or septicaemia (blood poisoning). Many animals and people carry Salmonella without showing any clinical signs, yet shed the bacteria in their faeces which can infect others.

Prevention, through proper hygiene, is the best way to control the disease and stop any spread to humans. Since most snakes which carry Salmonella are not ill they do not usually require treatment (which often fails to kill the bacterium anyway).

Septicaemia/toxaemia

Septicaemia or toxaemia is a condition where microbes such as bacteria or toxins invade the bloodstream and organs. Snakes with septicaemia are critically ill and are often near death. They exhibit lethargy, lack of appetite, open-mouth breathing and often have a red discoloration on the scales of their bellies. The condition is a true emergency that requires aggressive treatment in the hospital. Antibiotics, fluid therapy and force feeding are needed in an attempt to save the snake.

Incomplete shedding

Snakes may have difficulty shedding their skin. Often this is due to improper environmental temperature or low humidity. A special concern is the snake with retained spectacles (eye caps). The spectacles are normally shed during the shedding process. If they are retained a veterinary surgeon should be consulted about removal. Improper removal can result in permanent eye damage and blindness so preventing shedding problems is far preferable to curing. Talk to a vet about ways to increase humidity since low humidity may be a cause of retained eyecaps. Another cause is mite infestation.

Signs of illness in snakes may be specific for a certain disease, such as the cottage-cheese discharge in mouth rot, or non-specific, such as a snake with anorexia (lack of appetite) and lethargy. Any deviation from normal requires immediate evaluation by a veterinary surgeon.

TERRAPINS
& TORTOISES

Chelonia (tortoises, turtles and terrapins) are kept quite commonly. As with other reptiles different species live in varying habitats and thus have a variety of different environmental and dietary requirements in captivity. Investigating and providing the appropriate diet and environment is one of the main reasons why keeping a reptile can be interesting and challenging.

FEEDING

As with all reptile groups different species have different diets, but the Mediterranean tortoises (the most common in Britain) eat green plants almost exclusively. A prospective owner should discuss a specific diet with a veterinary surgeon. Frequency of eating varies but most young tortoises eat daily; older ones can be fed daily or every other day.

Most (80-90%) of a tortoise's plant material should be flowers and vegetables and the rest should be fruits. As a rule, anything green and leafy should make up a large part of the diet plus yellow and orange vegetables. Fibre-rich, vitamin-deficient vegetables including lettuce and celery should be avoided; their composition is mainly fibre and water with few vitamins or minerals.

Acceptable vegetables include mixed greens, cucumber, parsley, spinach (in small amounts), green beans, peas, cabbage or broccoli (also in small amounts) and flowers such as carnations and roses (avoid azaleas as they are toxic). Chickweed is especially good as it is high in calcium.

Vegetables can be offered cooked or raw (thoroughly washed) to see which the tortoise prefers. Flowers can be home-grown or bought. Often, flower shops throw out older, wilting blooms. While these may be unacceptable for sale to the public, reptile-owners can often get them free. It is wise to be sure that no chemicals have been applied to the flowers or water.

Fruit can include apples, pears, bananas, grapes, peaches, kiwis and melons. Fruits that are particularly healthy include figs (which contain calcium), papaya, raspberries and strawberries.

If the owner and vet decide that a small amount of animal-based protein is acceptable, appropriate foods include crickets, sardines (drained) and meal worms. Dog food and cat food generally contain too much vitamin D and fat so should probably be avoided. Reptile pellets, bird pellets, trout chow and other fish chows are excellent protein sources.

Live prey, such as crickets and worms, should either be raised by the owner, retrieved from a nearby field, or bought from a pet shop or reptile breeder. Care must be exercised when collecting insects, especially from the home garden, as fertilisers and insecticides can be toxic to chelonia.

Many veterinary surgeons recommend lightly sprinkling all the food offered to the tortoise with a calcium powder (calcium gluconate, lactate or carbonate). A light sprinkling of a good reptile vitamin supplement may be recommended. Over-supplementation with vitamins and minerals can cause problems in tortoises so owners should check with a vet for specific recommendations.

Fresh water in a ceramic dish that will not easily tip over should be available at all times. Tortoises will not only drink from the water bowl but will often bathe in it (although it is perfectly acceptable to mist the animal with water a few times a week too). The water should be kept clean; many tortoises love to defecate in their water bowl.

HOUSING

Tortoises can be housed outside during the summer in countries that have temperate climates, such as the UK. In the winter tortoises can be hibernated in a cool area such as an outhouse or kept active in a warmed environment. Animals which have not eaten adequately over the summer or who are ill should not be hibernated but most tortoises can safely be hibernated in a cool place overwinter. The options should be discussed with a veterinary surgeon. If the tortoise is awake through the winter and housed indoors, a ten- or 20-gallon aquarium is usually adequate.

Substrate, or bedding material, should be easy to clean and non-toxic to the tortoise. Newspaper, towels or even artificial turf is recommended. When using artificial turf, two pieces can be cut to fit the bottom of the cage. One should be put in the cage and the other kept clean. When the turf inside the cage becomes soiled it can be replaced with the spare piece and the soiled turf cleaned with ordinary soap and water, thoroughly rinsed and hung to dry to be used at the next cage cleaning.

Alfalfa pellets can also be used for bedding and are often eaten by the tortoise, which is acceptable. Avoid sand, gravel, wood shavings and cat litter, as these are not only difficult to clean but can cause impaction if eaten on purpose or if food becomes coated. Cedar wood shavings are toxic to reptiles!

Rocks (large ones) in the cage allow for basking. A hiding place is appreciated by all reptiles and should be available. Artificial plants can be arranged to provide a nook, as can clay pots, cardboard boxes and other containers.

A heat source is necessary for all reptiles, which are cold-blooded and need a range of temperatures to regulate their internal body temperature. Ideally, one end of the tank should be warmer than the other so that the tortoise can move around and warm or cool itself as needed. A thermometer at the cooler end of the cage should record 16-18°C (60°-65°F) and one at the warmer end should register 26-29°C (80-85°F). An inexpensive way to achieve these temperatures is to place a 100-watt incandescent bulb with a reflector hood outside and above one end of the cage, which should be covered by a screen top to prevent the tortoise from escaping or burning itself on the bulb. At night, heat is unnecessary as long as the temperature remains at 19-21°C (65-70°F).

Heating pads can be used instead and a veterinary surgeon can advise on the correct way to use them. Hot rocks or sizzle rocks are dangerous, ineffective and should be avoided!

Ultraviolet light is necessary to provide vitamin D-3. Without the light a tortoise will be predisposed to metabolic bone disease, a common condition of pet tortoises. Outside, of course, the sun provides adequate UV light.

The UV light should emit light in the UV-B range (290-320 nanometers). Combining a black light with a Vita-Lite, Chroma-50 or Colortone-50 in a two-bulb fixture is an excellent way to provide UV light, although many tortoises and turtles do well with just a Vita-Lite. A veterinary surgeon may recommend other brands of UV light that also provide a source of vitamin D-3.

The UV output of these lights decreases with age; they should be replaced every six months. For UV light to work, it must reach the pet in an unfiltered form, which means there must be no glass or plastic between the pet and the light. Finally, the light should be within 15-30 cm (6-12 inches) of the tortoise to be beneficial.

Tortoises housed outdoors should be in an enclosure or a walled garden. A shaded area should be provided, as well as a hiding area. Tortoises can dig out of enclosures, so bury the fencing 15-30 cm (6-12 inches) or put bricks or rocks under the area. Some owners find a children's paddling pool a suitable environment. Artificial turf can be used for lining material, or grass, twigs and other natural material will be fine if it is changed daily (avoid cedar as it is toxic to reptiles). Of course, food and fresh water must always be available. Bring the tortoise indoors if the temperature drops below 16°C (60°F). Finally, remember that tortoises can become prey for neighbourhood dogs, cats and tortoise rustlers so keep this in mind when housing outdoors.

Table 12

Biological data for selected species

	Spur-thighed tortoise (*Testudo graeca*)	Common box-tortoise (*Terrapene carolina*)	Red-eared terrapin (*Chrysemys scripta elegans*)
Region	Mediterranean	North America	North America
Environment			
Habitat	Terrestrial	Semi-aquatic	Semi-aquatic
Diet	Herbivorous* omnivorous	Carnivorous* frugivorous	Carnivorous
Temp. °C	20 - 27	22 - 27	20 - 22
Humidity %	50 - 70	60 - 80	80 - 90
Reproduction	Oviparous	Oviparous	Oviparous
Gestation (days)	60	50 - 90	59 - 93
Incubation temp. °C	28 - 32	25 - 30	25 - 30
Relative humidity %	90 - 100	30 - 32	80 - 100
Clutches/season	1 - 24		
Clutch size (eggs)	25 - 31	3 - 4	5 - 23
Longevity	50 years +	30 years +	20 years +
Shell length	15 - 20 cm	10 - 15 cm	25 cm (males smaller)

* Principal dietary requirements

COMMON DISEASES AND SPECIAL PROBLEMS

Signs of disease in these animals may be specific for a certain disease, such as nasal discharge in the case of a respiratory infection, or non-specific, such as a terrapin with anorexia (lack of appetite) and lethargy. Any deviation from normal should be a cause for concern and requires immediate evaluation by a veterinary surgeon, ideally one experienced in treating terrapins and tortoises.

Abscesses

Abscesses, common in pet terrapins and tortoises, appear as hard tumour-like swellings anywhere on the body. These are often related to vitamin A deficiency. They can be treated surgically: the abscess is opened and flushed with a medicated solution. A culture may be needed to determine the type of infection. Topical medication and injectable antibiotics may also be used.

Cystic calculi (bladder stones)

Commonly called bladder stones, these occur when minerals from the diet form crystals which then develop into stones. Generally these are composed of uric acid, which usually results from a diet that contains too much protein (such as a diet high in dog food or cat food). Blood in the droppings might be seen if a stone is present. An examination and radiographs (X-rays) allow a veterinary surgeon to diagnose the problem. Surgical removal of the stones is needed, as is fluid therapy to prevent kidney damage. A vet will advise dietary correction in an attempt to prevent future stones.

Parasites

Parasites, such as roundworms, are common in pet terrapins and tortoises. They often cause no clinical signs and are detected on an annual faecal examination. They may, however, cause diarrhoea or weight loss. They are treated with the appropriate deworming medication once the type of parasite has been identified under the microscope.

Respiratory disease

Most respiratory infections are caused by bacteria and, in terrapins, are often secondary to vitamin A deficiency. Terrapins and tortoises with respiratory infections may have excess mucus in their oral cavities, nasal discharge, lethargy, loss of appetite and possibly open-mouth breathing and wheezing. A veterinary surgeon may want to take radiographs (X-rays), blood tests and cultures to determine the cause of the infection. Occasionally, allergies or viral infections can cause nasal discharge. Treatment for true infections involves antibiotics given orally or as injections and possibly nose drops. Sick terrapins require intensive care, including fluid therapy and force feeding, in the hospital.

Salmonella

Tortoises and especially terrapins are infamous for carrying Salmonella. This bacterium can cause severe gastrointestinal disease or septicaemia (blood poisoning). Many animals and people carry the bacteria without showing any clinical signs yet shed the bacteria in their faeces which can infect others.

During the mid-1970s, it was discovered that many children contracted salmonellosis from their pet terrapins. Many of these children did not exercise proper hygiene (such as washing their hands after handling the animal). Prevention, through proper hygiene, is the best way to control the disease. Since most tortoises which carry Salmonella are not ill, they usually require no treatment (treatment often fails to kill the bacterium anyway).

Shell problems

Shell problems are often encountered, more in terrapins than tortoises because of their aquatic lifestyle. These can be infections caused by bacteria, fungi or viruses or, more commonly, the result of fractures of the shell. These can usually be repaired. Two common problems in tortoises are lawnmower injuries and severe burns from hibernating in garden refuse used in a bonfire. The former require reconstruction with fibre glass and a body filler. While the latter present severe problems with fluid loss and septicaemia both require specialist attention. Infections are more difficult to treat and involve identifying the organism (virus, bacterium or fungus), cleaning the shell thoroughly and using appropriate antimicrobial therapy.

Vitamin A

Vitamin A deficiency results from feeding an inappropriate diet, rather more in terrapins than tortoises but to some degree in each species. The all-meat diet, the "cricket and fruit cocktail" diet or the "lettuce and carrots" diet are all deficient. Lack of vitamin A produces changes in the epidermis (outer layer of skin and mucous membranes), lack of appetite, lethargy, swelling of the eyes and eyelids (often with a pus-type discharge), swelling of the ear (actually an ear abscess) and respiratory infections. The deficiency can be treated with oral vitamin A. Treatment should be under veterinary supervision as overdosing can occur and cause hypervitaminosis A.

Fig. 18

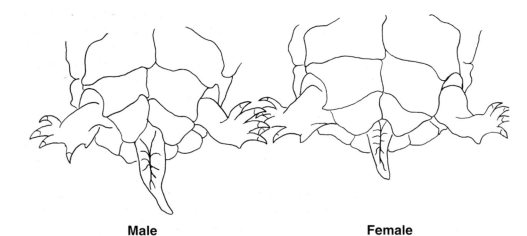

Male　　　　　　　　　　　　**Female**

External genitalia of adult tortoises.

Note male has broader and longer tail.

PREPARING FOR HIBERNATION

The key to maintaining any exotic pet in captivity is to imitate his/her natural environment as closely as possible. This does not mean providing a captive situation which looks from our perspective like the wild one, but rather one to which the animal's anatomy and physiology is adapted. Mediterranean tortoises are in a difficult situation: they can normally survive in a temperate summer climate such as Britain's and can be fed on vegetable matter but without careful maintenance over the winter they can die. This means preparing them for hibernation, assessing whether they are fit to hibernate, giving them appropriate hibernation conditions, monitoring them during hibernation and then being prepared to treat them for post-hibernational problems.

Mediterranean tortoises hibernate in their normal southern Mediterranean climate, but only for a limited time. The cold in this country is often too long for hibernation to be uneventful. Also, the summer is not always warm enough to allow a good nutritional and metabolic plane to be reached. For these reasons every tortoise should have a veterinary examination before hibernation is started. If a tortoise shows any clinical abnormalities it is foolish not to undertake as full an assessment as possible and this may mean taking a blood sample or an X-ray.

The autumn equinox (late September in the Northern hemisphere) is a watershed in deciding whether to commit a tortoise to hibernation. By this time he should have been checked, weighed and prepared for hibernation or taken into a warm environment for overwintering.

One of the critical, yet very easy, steps that should be performed when considering whether to hibernate a tortoise is to weigh and measure the animal. In the 1970s Dr Oliphant Jackson devised a simple graph showing the optimum weight for any given length of shell of Mediterranean tortoises. The weight of the tortoise divided by the shell length, the Jackson ratio, is now well known and a veterinary surgeon will find the graph in the British Small Animal Veterinary Association's Exotic Pets Manual. This graph will indicate whether the tortoise has put on enough weight over the summer to be able to hibernate.

The vet will want to look in the tortoise's mouth and ensure there is no infection, no discharge from the nose or any other orifice and feel the hindlimb musculature and the abdomen where the limbs exit through the shell. This is to ensure that there is sufficient body mass which is a little difficult, given that the shell hides so much of the body. A tortoise loses about 1% of his bodyweight per month of hibernation so one below the optimum Jackson ratio will lose too much, especially where hibernation occurs for up to six months. Thus, an underweight tortoise should not be allowed to hibernate. An overweight animal is unlikely to have excess muscle or fat gain but to have retained fluid, perhaps because of liver or kidney abnormality. Clearly any ill tortoise should be fully investigated and overwintered indoors, not hibernated.

A tortoise whose hibernation is deemed safe should be prevented from feeding for two to four weeks, as undigested food in the intestine ferments and causes problems. He/she should be encouraged to drink as much as required. In the falling temperatures of autumn reduced eating is, anyway, to be expected. The optimal temperature in which to keep a tortoise is 5°C (41°F), while below 2°C (34°F) is dangerous because of freeze-related disease. Temperatures above 10°C (50°F) precipitate activity and encourage catabolism or 'over-metabolism', with weightloss of over 1% per month.

More and more tortoise owners are extending the autumn artificially, in terms of light and temperature, so that the tortoise is not hibernated until perhaps mid-December. Terrapins living naturally in warmer climates do not generally hibernate and should be maintained in heated aquaria over winter. Although some can survive submerged outside this is not ideal.

MANAGING HIBERNATION

For many this used to mean putting the tortoise in a box in October and seeing if he awakened in the spring. For general welfare reasons and especially now that some tortoises are threatened with extinction (Greek spur-thighed and Hermann's) we should be even more careful to treat every tortoise as a valuable animal and be much more careful about managing its hibernation. Hibernation should be controlled by providing an indoor heated environment before and/or after a defined hibernation period as well as a monitored environment during hibernation. The environment should be monitored and check the animal regularly, not just when spring arrives.

A Mediterranean tortoise hibernating in a controlled manner requires a clean box containing bedding such as hay, with surrounding polystyrene insulation. Ideally a thermometer in the box should have a digital display of the interior temperature outside the insulation. A lid which is easy to open is important for frequent checks.

A tortoise should be awakened from hibernation if it urinates, since continued hibernation can lead to severe dehydration. If he has urinated he should be warmed gradually, awakened and encouraged to drink before continuing in a warm environment. If he has a discharge from mouth or nostrils he should be warmed, awakened and taken to a veterinary surgeon for a full exam. If the temperature falls below 2°C (34°F) it should be raised and, in spring when it is around 10°C (50°F) hibernation should end. An animal which has awakened, for whatever reason, should be overwintered for the remaining period before spring in a warmed environment and not allowed to hibernate for the rest of the winter.

A tortoise may be overwintered for the entire hibernation period if ill, if young or with a low Jackson ratio. He can be overwintered for the latter part of a winter if it urinates or if an early warm period awakens him. A Mediterranean tortoise should be kept at 18-25°C (62-77°F) during the day falling to 14-16°C (58-60°F) at night. Given that many overwintering tortoises suffer from dry eyes and skin; pots of gravel soaked with water should be provided to produce adequate humidity. Bright illumination is essential to encourage feeding - a 100-150W incandescent bulb is sufficient, but vitamin D production requires an ultraviolet tru-light. An overwintering tortoise can be placed in a shallow tepid bath but a bathing area should also be provided in his enclosure.

PROBLEMS AFTER HIBERNATION

When tortoises were plentiful people did not generally bother to take their tortoises to a vet before or after hibernation. Now that they are rare in the wild and hard to come by in captivity, things are very different and owners should be on the lookout for problems after hibernation in a cold climate such as ours.

Anorexia

After hibernation, especially if it is prolonged, a major problem is post-hibernational anorexia. The reason for failure to eat after waking from the winter may be pathological (a disease process), physiological (the animal taking time to eat even though healthy) or environmental (spring still too cold to encourage a return to feeding).

Thus, we can divide post-hibernational anorexia (PHA) into complicated (or pathological) or uncomplicated (i.e. physiological or environmental). The veterinary surgeon will need to take a full history of the tortoise before, during and after hibernation and perform a full clinical examination. If no other obvious abnormalities are noted the tortoise has uncomplicated PHA. It will probably be lighter in weight than would be expected from its shell length. A blood sample will probably show sugar is too low and urea higher than normal. Urea is a product of breakdown of proteins and is normally excreted in the urine but can build up over the period of hibernation to dangerously high levels.

The tortoise may be dehydrated, this being the reason for its high blood urea. This can be remedied by giving fluid by mouth to flush the urea out through the kidneys, making the animal urinate and starting to feed him either normally or via stomach tube. Improving husbandry, to provide optimal conditions while ensuring adequate fluid and energy input, solves the majority of problems in uncomplicated PHA.

In complicated or pathological PHA the anorexia is only one feature of a more serious disease, perhaps a bacterial infection. In fact the two most common conditions accompanying PHA are necrotic stomatitis (mouth rot) and runny nose syndrome (upper respiratory tract infection). These need local and systemic antibiotic therapy, although a runny nose probably has a viral cause as well as the bacteria which enter as secondary players.

Freeze damage

The other common problem after hibernation is related to freeze-damage. A tortoise hibernated in temperatures below 2°C (34°F) will experience some degree of tissue damage from the low temperatures and below 0°C (32°F) ice crystals form in the eye and the brain. This leads to cataract formation, damage to the retina at the back of the eye and permanent nerve damage. Blindness from these changes results in failure to see food and eat adequately, giving another cause for failure to eat, the problem of so much ill-health after hibernation.

These problems can be avoided by managing a tortoise's hibernation, keeping it shorter than it would be naturally in cold long winters and ensuring that the tortoise is not subjected to extremely low temperatures.

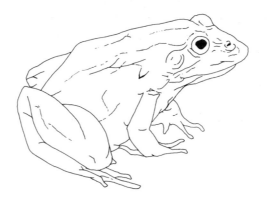

AMPHIBIANS

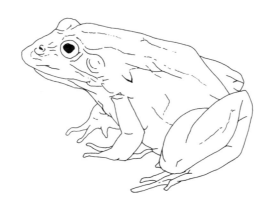

AMPHIBIANS

Amphibians (frogs, toads, newts, salamanders and the axolotl) are a diverse group of cold-blooded animals which, compared with mammals, birds and reptiles, have been overlooked as pets. They are relatively easy to keep and can be fascinating to study, though not easy to cuddle or take for a walk!

One of the most amazing things about amphibians is how they have taken the basic theme of being cold-blooded, having a thin moist skin and needing to return to water to breed, and adapted it to all sorts of environments across the world.

This means that different groups of amphibians need varied environments in which to survive and thrive but some generalisations can be made. They all need to be kept moist. Some, like the African clawed toad, live all the time under water and need an aquarium. The majority are terrestrial (land-dwelling) or arboreal (tree-dwelling) so can be kept in a vivarium with regular spraying to keep up the humidity.

SELECTION

The wide range of amphibians might make it difficult to decide which one to start with but some are easy to keep while others are more fragile and require a precisely controlled environment or have a voracious appetite and aggressive nature!

Fire-bellied toads

Fire-bellied toads are bright, attractive and interesting amphibians. The common fire-bellied toad (*Bombina bomina*) is an Asian species with a green and black back and an underside of grey or black marked with red or orange spots. The oriental fire-bellied toad (*Bombina orientalis*) is similar but a bit larger (around three inches long) with a brighter red belly. These species can be kept in a vivarium at the sort of temperature maintained in a centrally-heated house, although at times this can be a bit too cold.

Common frogs

The European tree frog (*Hyla arborea*) is another good species to keep in a vivarium inside. As its common and scientific names suggest, it likes a tall vivarium with plenty of plants to climb. The green tree frog (*Hyla cinerea*) is from the United States and is larger and less hardy than its European cousin, needing a warmer environment.

The Leopard frog (*Rana pipiens*) is an attractive, if not highly colourful frog from North America which would do well inside or outdoors. Do not keep this or any other foreign species free outside since it may escape and it is illegal to release non-endemic species into the countryside.

Another North American amphibian worth keeping is the Bullfrog (*Rana catesbiena*) which can grow to eight inches long. They generally do well outside in summer but need to be hibernated in winter. They have huge appetites and are happy to devour any smaller amphibians you are foolish enough to house with them!

Horned frogs and clawed toads

These horned amphibians (*Ceratophrys* species) are South American land-dwellers. They are large attractive but are aggressive enough to attack and eat others of their own species. They are not suitable for beginners.

The African clawed toad (*Xenopus laevis*) is entirely aquatic and should be kept in an aquarium, but one with a filtration system and supplementary heating during winter. It can be fed on meat, in which case be sure to add adequate minerals and vitamins.

Tropical frogs

White's tree frog (*Litoria caerulea*) is a beautiful species from Australia and New Guinea, which requires a tropical vivarium between 25°C (77°F) and 30°C (86°F) with high humidity. For this reason it is not ideal as a starter amphibian.

The same can be said for poison arrow frogs (*Dendrobates* species). These brightly-coloured tiny expensive frogs from South America need a tropical environment and, as their name suggests, are poisonous with highly toxic skin secretions. They should be kept only by herpetologists with considerable experience of tropical amphibia. Another toxic species is the fire salamander (*Salamandra salamandra*) which has poisionous secretions from its salivary glands. It should be handled at all times with gloves.

The axolotl

A fascinating species from a biological as well as a visual perspective is the axolotl (*Ambystoma mexicanum*). This creature lives its whole life as a huge tadpole and it never metamorphoses into the adult salamander it was meant to be! It even breeds as a larval form and can grow to nine or ten inches long. It should be kept in filtered and well oxygenated water but does not need heating in winter if in a centrally-heated house.

Whichever amphibian appeals to a prospective owner, it should not be bought without first thinking about the environment necessary. Far too many amphibians fare very poorly in captivity because their environment does not meet their requirements. Given a little thought and attention, amphibians can be fascinating to keep. They amply repay the time and effort spent making sure they are housed correctly.

HANDLING

As they have moist and reasonably fragile skin, amphibians should be handled carefully with moistened hands or while wearing wet plastic gloves. This protects the animal and you from any toxic substance they might produce. Toads are especially liable to do this. As they can absorb chemicals through the skin it is a good idea to wash your hands before picking them up, making sure you rinse off any detergent.

FEEDING

Amphibians almost invariably need to be fed live food. Most adults can be fed invertebrates, either wild-caught such as earthworms and slugs, or captive-reared such as wax moth larvae, meal worms and crickets. Aquatic species thrive on live food sold for feeding to fish. The key in any diet is to avoid repetition, which is boring for the animal and nutritionally unbalanced. The same can be said for feeding only raw meat rather than whole prey items. Feeding the whole individual, be it a small fish or an earthworm, gives a wide range of minerals and vitamins while meat on its own is low in calcium and vitamins. If larger toads and frogs are fed on such a diet a vitamin and mineral supplement should be given.

COMMON PROBLEMS

Failure to feed

Failure to feed may be part of a condition known as maladaptation syndrome. Here a host of factors is not quite right: temperature, humidity, light and diet all conspire to put the amphibian off feeding. Anorexia merely adds to the downward spiral and, unless conditions change to mimic the amphibian's natural habitat, he is unlikely to recover.

Red leg

Red leg is a skin condition which is an outward sign of a generalised bacterial infection. This may be related to unhygienic conditions where the water in the vivarium or aquarium is not changed often enough. Affected animals should be removed from other members of the colony to a hospital tank where they can be treated with antibiotics. Such a tank can be a large lunch box with a piece of moist foam rubber on which the patients can climb. The vivarium should be thoroughly cleaned while the sick amphibians are undergoing hospital treatment.

INVERTEBRATES

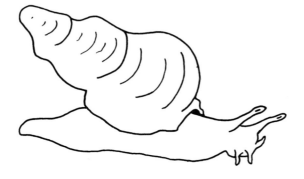

SCORPIONS
& TARANTULAS

Scorpions and tarantulas are the most fascinating and some of the most visually striking terrestrial invertebrates. They are members of the arthropod class arachnidae, having eight legs and simple eyes, rather than the compound eyes of the insects.

SCORPIONS

There are around 600 species of scorpion distributed around the world, some of them small and very poisonous, others large, black and not particularly dangerous. It is these latter species, the emperor scorpions (*Pandinus imperator*) which are most common in pet shops.

These scorpions can be kept in a glass or plastic tank with a close-fitting lid but with good ventilation. The bottom of the tank can be covered with bark, wood chippings or vermiculite which looks good, but scorpions seem equally happy with newspaper, as long as there is a hiding place under a broken flower pot or piece of bark.

Fresh water should always be available and a misting with a water spray should be used on occasion, although it is easy to saturate the bedding, with subsequent growth of mould. This must be avoided at all costs. Scorpions should be fed on live insects; crickets are available in many pet shops. Jungle scorpions can eat three or four crickets a week and over-feed themselves. Remember that in the wild these animals catch prey only every so often and they cannot easily adjust to having a copious supply in captivity. A scorpion which overfeeds will have a distended abdomen and should be fed perhaps one cricket every month of so until the corpulence subsides.

TARANTULAS

The mygalomorph spiders have, for many years, been termed tarantulas. This is erroneous. The true tarantula spider is a much smaller European species while the so-called tarantulas are Central or South American spiders with some Asian species. They have the misfortune to be called 'bird-eating spiders' but while they might take fledglings as carrion, they are much more likely to feed on small invertebrates.

While these spiders look dangerous and will bite if annoyed, they are not highly venomous. The more dangerous side to tarantulas is that they have so-called urticarial hairs on their backs and, if harassed, they will rub these off with their back legs, giving the bare patch seen on many tarantulas in captivity. These hairs can cause a skin reaction or, if inhaled, a more serious respiratory asthma-like attack.

SELECTION

Species such as the red knee, the pink toe, the Chilean Rose (*Grammostola cala*) the Chilean Yellow Rump (*Phtixotrichus auratus*), the Mexican red rump (*Brachypelma vagans*) and the White collared (*Pterinopelma saltator*) are all good spiders for beginners. Aggressive spiders such as the Haitian Brown (*Phormictopus cancerides*), the Trinidad Chevron (*Psalmopoeus cambridgei*) and the Thai Black (*Melopoeus albostriatus*) are not good for a beginner. In fact there is probably not a good reason why anyone should keep these species.

A tarantula should not be kept as a way of impressing friends but rather as a fascinating and unusual biological specimen.

HOUSING

Tarantulas should be housed in a glass or plastic vivarium with a well-ventilated but closely-fitting lid. The vivarium floor should be covered with bark chippings or vermiculite, with a hiding place provided. Tarantulas live in different habitats and each should be given a vivarium environment appropriate to their natural lifestyle. Some such as the pink toe *Avicularia avicularia* has an arboreal (tree-dwelling) habitat while the Mexican red knee *Brachypelma smithii* can be found in trees or in ground burrows. These two species are particularly good for beginners, as they are docile. The only problem is that the red knee has been overtrapped in its native habitat and is under international import regulation.

This takes us on to the subject of breeding. As more people have a particular interest in these spiders and gain expertise in keeping and breeding them, there will be more captive-breds which will reduce the need to import them.

COMMON PROBLEMS

People tend to overfeed their pet tarantulas; in the wild they might only have a prey item every month and so feeding a cricket a week or more may well result in a period of anorexia. This may simply correct itself after the spider has regained its normal weight but may require a reduction in temperature for a while followed by restoration of a tropical climate to simulate seasonal change.

Dysecdysis is the long scientific term for a problem with skin shedding. Tarantulas need a reasonably humid environment in which to shed and problems may occur if this is not provided. Shedding very often involves the spider turning upside down for a while. Owners should be advised of this since the spider should not be touched during this period but the temptation is to pick the animal up to place it the right way up! While female spiders live for a considerable time as an adult after their last developmental moult, males may actually die after quite a short time as a sexually active adult.

If a spider loses a leg in an accident it may well regrow after a month but this new leg may start out small and give problems in shedding. Some gentle assistance can be given over this period by someone with experience in spider husbandry.

GIANT AFRICAN LAND SNAILS

These snails of the *Achatina* species are large and can grow to over 20 cm (5 ins). They are fascinating creatures, with relatively simple husbandry requirements. Although tropical or subtropical in origin they survive well in the ambient temperature of a well heated house.

Snails are hermaphrodite, i.e. every individual is both male and female. They cannot mate with themselves but form a slime-covered pairing after which eggs are laid.

They can be fed on household vegetable and fruit scraps and waste, their only key dietary requirement being calcium for their shells. This can be provided by giving powdered egg shell in an otherwise totally vegetable diet.

They have few health problems and those which do occur are not particularly well understood from a veterinary perspective. One is leucoderma or small white patches on the skin of the 'foot' or main body. Whether this is infectious or not is unclear but your vet will be able to investigate the problem or refer you to someone with a special interest in these animals.

One potentially problematic disease is the lungworm *Angiostrongylus cantonensis*. These snails are a host for the larvae of this worm in the Far East which is a concern given that it can be passed to humans and is a cause of menigitis. However, no animals in the West have been found to carry this parasite. It must be emphasised that you should always wash your hands after dealing with snails, or any other pet.

Glossary

Arboreal   -   *living in trees*

Carnivorous   -   *feeding on flesh or other animal matter*

Frugivorous   -   *feeding on fruit*

Herbivorous   -   *feeding on plants*

Insectivorous   -   *feeding on insects also on plants that capture and absorb insects*

Omnivorous   -   *feeding on many kinds of food, especially both plants and flesh*

Oviparous   -   *laying eggs*

Semi-aquatic   -   *living partly in water and partly on land*

Terrestrial   -   *living on land*

Viviparous   -   *bearing live young*

Index

USEFUL ADDRESSES

Animal Health Trust, Lanwades Park, Kentford, Newmarket, Suffolk CB8 7UU.
Tel: 01638 751000 Fax: 01638 750448.

British Chelonia Group, General Secretary, The Paddock, 47 Hillcorner Road,
Chippenham, Wilts. SN15 1DP.
Tel: 01249 462375

British Rabbit Council, Purefoy House, 7 Kirkgate, Newark, Nottingham NG24 1AD
Tel: 01636 676042 Fax: 01636 611683

British Small Animal Veterinary Association, Kingsley House, Church Lane,
Shurdington, Cheltenham, Glos. GL51 5TQ.
Tel: 01242 862994. Fax: 01242 863009.

British Veterinary Association (BVA), 7 Mansfield Street, London WIM OAT.
Tel: 0171 636 6541 Fax: 0171 436 2970

British Veterinary Nursing Association, Level 15, Terminus House, Terminus Street,
Harlow, Essex CM20 1XA
Tel. 01279 450567 Fax: 01279 420866

National Fancy Rat Society, 26 King's Orchard, Eltham, London SE9 5TJ.

National Hamster Council, P.O. Box 154, Rotherham, S. Yorks. S66 OFI.
Tel: 01709 531007.

National Mouse Club, 22 Malham Road, Rastrick, Brighouse,
West Yorkshire. HD6 3JY.

People's Dispensary for Sick Animals, Whitechapel Way, Priorslee, Telford,
Shropshire. TF2 9PQ. Tel. 01952 290999

Proteus Reptile Rescue & Sanctuary, 204 Slade Road, Erdington,
Birmingham B23 7RJ.

Rare Breeds Survival Trust, 4th St., National Agricultural Centre, Kenilworth,
Warwickshire. CV8 2LG. Tel. 01203 696551

Royal College of Veterinary Surgeons, Belgravia House, 62-64 Horseferry Road,
London SW1P 2AF. Tel: 0171 222 2001. Fax: 0171 222 2004.

Royal Society for the Protection of Cruelty to Animals (RSPCA), The Causeway,
Horsham, West Sussex. RH12 1HG. Tel: 01403 264181.

Society for Companion Animal Studies (SCAS), 10(b) Leny Road, Callender, Perthshire. FK17 8BA.

The Blue Cross, 1 Hugh Street, London SW1V 1QQ. Tel: 0171 834 1128.

The Mammal Society, 15 Cloisters House, 8 Battersea Park Road, London SW8 4BG. Tel: 0171 498 4358 Fax: 0171 498 4459.

The National Ferret School, P.O. Box 61, Chesterfield S42 6ZX.

Wood Green Animal Shelters, Kings Bush Far, London Road, Godmanchester, Cambridgeshire PE18 8LJ. Tel: 01480 830014 Fax: 01480 830158.

Zoological Society of London, Regent's Park, London NW1 4RY. Tel: 0171 722 3333 Fax: 0171 586 2870.

FURTHER READING

Beynon, P.H. & Cooper, J. E. (*Eds*) (1991)
BSAVA Manual of Exotic Pets.

Beynon, P.H., Lawton, M. P.C. & Cooper, J.E. (*Eds*) (1992)
BSAVA Manual of Reptiles.

Harkness, J. E. & Wagner, J.E. (1989)
The biology and medicine of rabbits and rodents.
3rd ed. Lea & Febiger, Philadelphia and London.

Hillyer, Elizabeth V. and Quesenberry, Katherine (1997)
Ferrets, Rabbits and Rodents. Clinical Medicine and Surgery.
W. B. Saunders

Laber-Laird, K. Swindle, M. M. & Flecknell, P.A. (1996)
Handbook of Rodent & Rabbit Medicine.
Oxford Pergamon Press.

Mader, D. R. (1996)
Reptile Medicine and Surgery.
W. B. Saunders Company.

Mattison, C. (1987)
The care of reptiles and amphibians in captivity. 2nd edition.
Blandford Press, Poole.

McArthur, S. (1998)
Veterinary Management of Tortoises and Turtles
Blackwell Science, Oxford

Notes

Notes

Notes

Notes